*PRODUCTION THEORY AND INDIVISIBLE COMMODITIES*

PRINCETON STUDIES IN MATHEMATICAL ECONOMICS

NUMBER III

# PRODUCTION THEORY AND INDIVISIBLE COMMODITIES



BY CHARLES R. FRANK, JR.

1969

PRINCETON UNIVERSITY PRESS
PRINCETON, NEW JERSEY

L. C. Card: 68-29383

Printed in the United States of America



This book has been composed in Monotype Baskerville type

*To my mother and father.*

# PREFACE

The analysis in this volume owes much to the pioneering work of writers such as Debreu,[1] Koopmans,[2] and Gale.[3] These theorists and others, by applying modern mathematical and logical techniques, examined some of the propositions of the classical theory of welfare economics. They stated the classical propositions precisely, proved them rigorously, and extended the analysis to cases not easily handled by the traditional tools of differential calculus. This book represents an attempt to apply modern mathematical techniques to another set of propositions which have arisen in the economic literature. The propositions examined here, however, tend to lie outside the framework of classical welfare economics.

Originally, the classical theory derived its validity from assumptions of diminishing returns and diminishing marginal utility. Modern theorists in the classical tradition have relied on more general assumptions, such as diminishing marginal rates of substitution and transformation. The classical theory reaches its most developed form in the works of Debreu in which the classical propositions are derived from assumptions about the convexity of production sets and consumer preferences. This theory, however, is not able to deal with the phenomenon of commodity indivisibility, which may cause a violation of all of the above assumptions.

Economic theorists have long been concerned with the problem of pricing and resource allocation under conditions of commodity indivisibility and increasing returns to scale. Writers such as Dupuit,[4] Hicks,[5] Pigou,[6] Lerner,[7] Jantzen,[8] Clark,[9] and Lewis[10] have dealt with these problems in detail. Out of the writings of these authors and others who have touched on these problems, the following rough and informal

[1] G. Debreu, *Theory of Value* (New York: Wiley, 1959).

[2] T. C. Koopmans, "Analysis of Production as an Efficient Combination of Activities," in T. C. Koopmans, ed., *Activity Analysis of Production and Allocation* (New York: Wiley, 1951).

[3] D. Gale, *The Theory of Linear Economic Models* (New York: McGraw Hill, 1960).

[4] Jules Dupuit, "De la Mésure de l'Utilité des Travaux Publiques," *Annales des Ponts et Chausées*, 2nd series, Vol. 8 (1844), reprinted in *International Economic Papers*, No. 2 (1952), pp. 83–110.

[5] J. R. Hicks, "The Rehabilitation of Consumers Surplus," *Review of Economic Studies*, Vol. VIII (Feb. 1941), pp. 108–116.

[6] A. C. Pigou, *The Economics of Welfare*, 4th ed. (London: Macmillan, 1938).

[7] A. P. Lerner, *The Economics of Control* (New York: Macmillan, 1944).

[8] I. Jantzen, "Laws of Production Cost," *Econometrica*, Vol. 16 (Jan. 1948), pp. 44–48.

[9] J. M. Clark, *Studies in the Economics of Overhead Costs* (Chicago: Chicago University Press, 1923).

[10] W. A. Lewis, *Overhead Cost* (London: Allen, 1949).

set of propositions can be derived: If there are indivisible commodities or increasing returns to scale then:

1) Perfectly competitive, profit-maximizing entrepreneurs do not allocate resources efficiently—efficient allocation requires a scheme of discriminatory pricing;
2) In order to effect efficient allocation, producers must have some means of covering the cost of lumpy or indivisible inputs—this requires subsidization;
3) When indivisibilities are present, efficient allocation of resources is not achieved if each commodity has a separate price—different commodities must be priced together as a package;
4) If divisible inputs are substitutable for lumpy inputs, then indivisible commodities do not cause any modifications of the classical theory; and
5) Indivisibilities are only important when production takes place on a small scale—at larger scales of operation one can effectively assume away the problem of indivisibilities.

The analysis in this volume supports each one of these propositions. Thus there is little said in the author's work which cannot be found in one form or another in the past literature. The author's intent, however, is to provide the beginnings of a general, systematic, and rigorous analysis of the problems of indivisibilities. The volume is no more than a beginning, since many of the assumptions are quite restrictive and the consumer sector of the economy is hardly discussed. Much more needs to be done before a satisfactory theory emerges. The author hopes that he has made a start in the right direction.

The ideas developed in this work grew out of the author's Ph.D. dissertation presented in June 1963 to the Department of Economics of Princeton University. The author's largest debt is to the chairman of his dissertation committee, Professor Harold W. Kuhn. He suggested the topic and provided guidance, suggestions, and encouragement at nearly every step along the way. Professor William J. Baumol, the other member of the dissertation committee, was very helpful in providing detailed comments and suggestions on preliminary drafts of the dissertation. My wife, Susan Patricia Frank, helped in tracking down source materials and tolerated an often-working husband trying to meet a June deadline in the first few months of marriage.

The present manuscript is a substantially revised version of the original dissertation. Some proofs have been modified, a number of errors eliminated, illustrations provided, the exposition revised, and the analysis expanded. Professor Kuhn and two anonymous readers were especially helpful in these revisions. Mrs. Manya Vas and Mrs. Jane Huyeck admirably performed various typing chores. Mrs. Doris Garvey assisted in checking all the references. Responsibility for the final product, of course, lies with the author.

The plan of the book falls into two parts: (*a*) Chapters 2 through 5—an analysis of a very general model of production, emphasizing the problems of indivisibilities and increasing returns to scale; and (*b*) Chapter 6—a final section on an integer activity analysis of production and allocation. Chapters 1 and 7 form an introduction and a conclusion. A mathematical appendix follows Chapter 7. This appendix contains all the relevant mathematical definitions, lemmas, and theorems and some of the proofs. The appendix represents an attempt to make the volume self-contained. The reader may wish to cover the appendix first or use it as a reference in going through the text.

In relation to the original dissertation, the second part has undergone the most substantial change. In the original version, the periodic structure of solutions to integer programming problems was investigated for the single constraint and single activity cases. The pricing and resource allocation implications of this periodic structure were also explored. Since the dissertation was written, however, Ralph Gomory, working independently, has published proofs of a number of similar propositions concerning the periodic nature of solutions to a much more general class of integer programming problems.[11] Chapter 6 has been revised along the lines suggested by Gomory's article and the implications for pricing and resource allocation have been drawn within the context of a general activity analysis model of production.

Charles R. Frank, Jr.
Princeton, March 1968

[11] R. Gomory, "On the Relation between Integer and Non-Integer Solutions to Linear Programs," *Proceedings of the National Academy of Sciences*, Vol. 53 (Feb. 1965), pp. 260–265.

# *CONTENTS*

# *PRODUCTION THEORY AND INDIVISIBLE COMMODITIES*

# CHAPTER 1

# *INTRODUCTION*

## 1.1 Indivisible Commodities

Economic theory, if it is to be useful at all, must be abstract. That is, some postulates may not conform completely to all the facts. This may be necessary to engage in logical analysis and arrive at specific conclusions, but postulates should emphasize those facts which are particularly relevant to the problem at hand. The conclusions reached on the basis of such postulates must be meaningful or valid with respect to any policy decisions which have to be made. Although the economic theorist may make simplifying postulates and ignore certain variables, he must guard against the tendency to choose his postulates solely on the basis of building a model which is easily manipulated.[1]

One of the usual assumptions in economic theory is that commodities can be measured by real numbers. Production functions, demand curves, and cost functions are assumed to be defined for real number arrays and to behave properly with respect to various criteria of continuity. Assumptions of this sort simplify economic analysis. They imply, however, an acceptance of commodity divisibility[2] and ignore the difficulty or even impossibility, in practice, of using or producing fractional units of a commodity. In many instances indivisible rather than divisible commodities are the more relevant with which to deal.

This book incorporates the notion of indivisibility in a limited way into an analysis of production and allocation in the belief that there is a large class of problems for which this type of analysis is important. In some instances we make drastically simple assumptions to provide a basis for meaningful analysis.

## 1.2 Efficiency and Pareto Optimality

Frequently it is useful to divide an economy into two sectors—the production sector and the consumption sector. In the production sector, inputs of various commodities may be combined to produce outputs of various other commodities. A set of numbers specifying the amount of each input and each output is called an input-output combination. If we

[1] For a discussion of the relationship between theory and practice, see Paul Samuelson, *Economics: An Introductory Analysis* (5th ed., New York: McGraw Hill, 1961) pp. 11–12. On realism in economic models see T. C. Koopmans, *Three Essays on the State of Economic Science* (New York: McGraw Hill, 1957), pp. 144–146.

[2] The mathematical economist usually makes such assumptions more explicitly than the economist who "verbalizes" his analysis, but commodity divisibility is usually implied by both.

ignore resource limitations, then an input-output combination is called a *possible* input-output combination if it is compatible with a given state of technology. If an input-output combination is compatible with the known state of technology and *also* with any resource restrictions, then it is called an *attainable* input-output combination. A possible (or attainable) input-output combination is an efficient input-output combination only if there is no other possible input-output combination which (*a*) results in more of one output with no less of any other output or with no more of any input or which (*b*) uses less of any input with no more of any other input or with no less of any output. Our definition of efficiency refers only to efficiency within the production sphere.

Each commodity is assigned a price. Associated with each possible input-output combination is a unique profit. A profit-maximizing input-output combination is one which gives the maximum profit over all possible input-output combinations.

In the consumption sector of the economy, there is a given number of consumers, each with a set of preferences (a partial ordering) for all commodity combinations. An input-output combination is Pareto optimal if there is no other attainable input-output combination which could make at least one consumer "better off" with no other consumer "worse off." Given some easily acceptable assumptions, one can show that every Pareto optimal input-output combination is efficient. In a sense one might say that every efficient input-output combination is a candidate as a point of Pareto optimality.

We can illustrate this in a simplified way in terms of Figure 1.1. Let $RR'$ represent an indifference curve for Robinson Crusoe.[3] Let the heavy dots in the shaded area represent the attainable combinations of the two indivisible goods $X$ and $Y$. Then the point $E$ is the most preferred combination from Robinson's point of view.

For any efficient point such as $B$, $C$, or $F$, one can draw a conceivable indifference curve for Robinson which would make such an efficient point the most preferred point from Robinson's point of view. Thus, every efficient point may possibly be socially desirable.

On the other hand, consider a point which is not efficient, such as $G$. Only a very strange preference pattern for Robinson would make such a point socially desirable. Only if Robinson were completely satiated with respect to one or the other of the commodities or if Robinson had a positive dislike for one of the commodities would such a point be a most

[3] $RR'$ is not really an indifference curve in the sense that Robinson is indifferent between any two points on the curve, since there are points on the curve which represent fractional amounts of the indivisible commodities $X$ and $Y$. Rather, we can view $RR'$ as a line which separates all commodity combinations which are preferred to $E$ (those combinations above and to the right of $RR'$) from those commodity bundles which are less preferred to $E$ (all points below $RR'$).

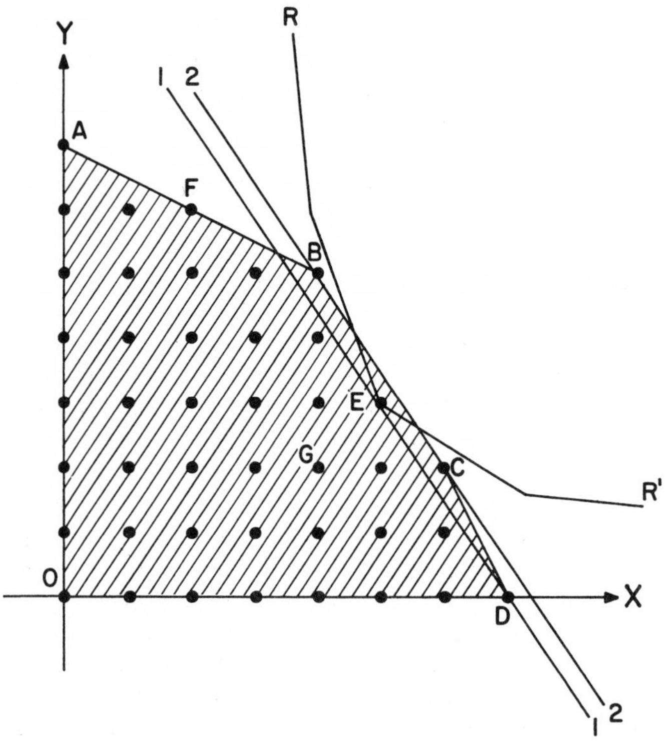


Figure 1.1

preferred feasible point. Thus, except for some types of social preferences, only efficient points seem to be candidates for social desirability.

We should like to keep the distinction between efficiency and Pareto optimality clear. *Efficiency* refers to the production sphere and *Pareto optimality* refers to both the production and the consumption sectors. Throughout a large part of this book, we shall consider only the criterion of efficiency and in such cases we shall limit most of our discussion to the production sector of the economy.

## 1.3 The Problem of Attaining Efficiency

Since any efficient point, and only an efficient point, is a candidate for Pareto optimality, it seems desirable that any efficient input-output combination should be profit-maximizing for some conceivable set of prices for each commodity. In other words, we wish to prove that every profit-maximizing input-output combination is efficient, and conversely, for each efficient input-output combination there exists a set of prices for which that efficient combination is profit-maximizing. If there are no indivisible commodities, then given certain reasonable assumptions, the theorem can be proved using the supporting hyperplane theorem of mathematical topology. The mathematical property of convexity of the set of feasible or possible points is necessary to prove the supporting hyperplane theorem. Where indivisibilities are present, the assumption of convexity on the set of production possibilities is precluded. "Convexity can be used with some degree of approximation only in problems where the granularity arising from indivisiblity of resources is unimportant."[4] We should note that one can prove that every profit-maximizing input-output combination is efficient without the aid of any convexity argument. The proof of the converse, however, breaks down in the absence of convexity.

Baumol[5] suggests a counterexample to disprove the converse where indivisibility is present. The counterexample can be demonstrated with the use of Figure 1.1. The heavy dots represent feasible production combinations of the two indivisible goods *X* and *Y*, given a certain amount of resources. The dots correspond to integer amounts of the two indivisible goods; no point representing fractional units of these goods is feasible. The shaded area is the convex hull of the set of feasible points, and line *OABCDO* is the boundary of the convex hull. One can loosely refer to the part of the boundary labeled *ABCD* as a transformation curve of the commodities *X* and *Y*. Assume all costs to be zero so that maximum profit corresponds to maximum revenue or the maximum valuation of the two products. Lines 1 and 2 are iso-value lines—lines of constant value or revenue obtained from the two products. All points above and to the right of an iso-value line are points of higher value; all points below correspond to a lower valuation. Given any positive set of prices, the maximum value of the two products will be attained only at a feasible point which lies on the boundary *ABCD*. A rough proof of this statement is as follows: Suppose some point, say *E* in Figure 1a, not on the boundary, were profit-maximizing. Then there would be points of the convex hull above and to the right of such a point, and therefore above and to the right of the iso-value line. Of all points above and to the right of the iso-value line there must be a feasible point such as *B* or *C*. If there were no such feasible points, then all points above and to the right of the iso-value line could be cut away from the convex hull, and the remaining part of the convex hull would be convex and also contain all feasible points. But this would contradict the definition of the convex hull. Thus, there must be feasible points such as *B* and *C* above the iso-value line, but such points would have a greater value than *E*, and therefore *E* is not profit-maximizing. This is a contradiction, and thus we have proved our assertion.

Now *E* is an efficient point in that there is no other feasible combination of goods *X* and *Y* above and to the right of *E*. But *E* is not profit-

[4] T. C. Koopmans, *Three Essays on the State of Economic Science*, p. 25.

[5] William J. Baumol, *Economic Theory and Operations Analysis* (Englewood Cliffs, New Jersey: Prentice Hall, 1961), pp. 327–330.

maximizing for any set of prices, as we have shown, since it does not lie on that part of the boundary of the convex hull labeled *ABCD*.

## 1.4 Plan of Attack

This volume contains seven chapters. Chapter 2 outlines a very general model of production and precisely defines the notions of pricing, efficiency, and profit maximization. Several of the traditional theorems of production theory which neither stand nor fall on the assumption of divisible commodities are also proved. In Chapter 3 indivisible commodities are carefully defined and introduced into the model. Constant and increasing returns to scale are also defined and discussed. Chapter 4 includes a discussion of the notions of price discrimination and commodity substitution. Chapter 5 outlines pertinent ways in which efficiency may be achieved in the presence of indivisible commodities. Efficient points may be attained with (*a*) subsidization, (*b*) an assumption that entrepreneurs "almost" maximize profits, (*c*) an assumption of substitution between divisible and indivisible commodities, and (*d*) price discrimination. Chapter 6 applies some of the analysis and concepts of previous chapters to the case where production is viewed as an efficient combination of activities which are restricted to integer levels. Several theorems concerning the properties of integer programs emerge.

# CHAPTER 2

# *PRODUCTION POSSIBILITIES, ATTAINABILITY, PRICES, EFFICIENCY, AND PROFIT MAXIMIZATION*

## 2.1 Introduction

This chapter is devoted to a partial review of modern theory of production.[1]

Four properties of the set of production possibilities, (A) additivity, (B) inaction, (C) disposal, and (D) closure, are used to prove some well-known theorems in the theory of production. No assumptions are made about commodity divisibility or convexity of the set of production possibilities; thus all theorems proved are independent of the convexity postulate. Theorems 2.9.1 and 2.9.2, concerning the convex hull of the set of production possibilities, will be needed in the development of later chapters.

## 2.2 Production Possibilities

Consider a vector $y = (y_i) = (y_1, y_2, \ldots, y_n)$ with $n$ real numbers as its elements. The set of all such points is called an $n$-dimensional Euclidean space, denoted by $E^n$. The $i^{\text{th}}$ co-ordinate of $y$ is $y_i$. The model of production which we shall consider will be characterized by a set $Y$ of points in the space $E^n$, called the set of production possibilities.

Definition 2.2.1. The set of production possibilities is a subset $Y$ of $E^n$.

Definition 2.2.2. Any point $y = (y_i) = (y_1, y_2, \ldots, y_n)$ is called a possible point. Each of the co-ordinates $y_i$ of a possible point $y$ represents the amount of a commodity.

Definition 2.2.3. A negative co-ordinate of a possible point $y$ is called an input. A positive co-ordinate of $y$ is an output.

The terms *set of production possibilities*, *possible point*, *commodity*, *output*, and *input* are all abstract terms without specific reference to real world entities. Although much of the analysis in this chapter and others will be concerned with pure abstractions, this does not preclude interpretation in terms of real world phenomena, but the distinction must be made clear.

[1] The discussion of this chapter is based to a large extent on Gerard Debreu, *Theory of Value* (New York: Wiley, 1959) pp. 37–49, passim, and on T. C. Koopmans, *Three Essays on the State of Economic Science* (New York: McGraw Hill, 1957) and "Analysis of Production as an Efficient Combination of Activities," in T. C. Koopmans, ed., *Activity Analysis of Production and Allocation* (New York: Wiley, 1951), pp. 33–97.

We shall try to indicate by tone and style when we are speaking purely in abstract terms and when we are attempting an interpretation. The purpose of keeping the discourse on a general and abstract level is to allow for the possibility of varied interpretation.

One can consider a set of production possibilities as the set of possible input-output combinations available to an economic agent or group of agents. The group of agents may be the managers of a particular plant in a firm, the managers of the entire firm, the managers of all firms in an industry, the inhabitants of a geographical region, or the citizens of a country. Any point $y$ in the production set is a list of outputs and inputs which is technically feasible, given the technical and engineering knowledge available to the agents. The set of production possibilities allows for joint production (more than one output), but does not take into account resource limitations.

Figure 2.1 illustrates a two-dimensional Euclidean space $E^2$ and a set of production possibilities $Y$ which is a subset of $E^2$. The horizontal axis represents the amount $y_1$ of commodity 1 and the vertical axis represents the amount of $y_2$ of commodity 2. The shaded area is the set $Y$ of production possibilities. Any point in the shaded area is a possible point. In particular, the point $y$ in Figure 2.1 is a possible point with commodity 1 as an input and commodity 2 as an output. The point $y'$ is possible, and both commodities are inputs. That is, it is possible to dispose of both commodities without producing anything.

Suppose that in Figure 2.1 commodities 1 and 2 are land and wine, respectively. Then $y$ indicates that it is possible to use land as an input to obtain wine as an output. The point $y'$ indicates that both land and

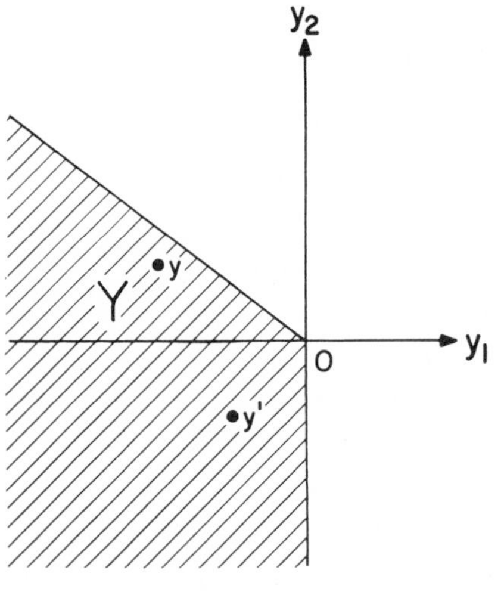


Figure 2.1

wine could be used as inputs without obtaining any outputs by disposal of both land and wine.

The concept of a set $Y$ of production possibilities is more general than the usual notion of a production function. For one thing, joint production (more than one output) is introduced in a very simple way. For example, suppose the point $y^* = (5, 4, -3, -7)$ is a possible point. This point represents a set of input and output coefficients for four different commodities. There are two outputs, produced in amounts of 5 and 4, and two inputs, used in amounts $-3$ and $-7$. Thus the point $y^*$ represents the joint production of two outputs by two inputs.

Secondly, the set of production possibilities allows for a richer set of technical possibilities than does a production function. It may be true that for a given combination of input and output coefficients for $n - 1$ of the commodities, varied amounts of the $n^{\text{th}}$ commodity may be possible. Such variations are permitted within the context of a *set* of production possibilities. With a *production function*, however, "the function must be so defined that it expresses the *maximum product* obtainable from the combination at the existing state of *technical* knowledge. Therefore, the purely *technical* maximization problem may be said to be solved by the very definition of our production function."[2]

## 2.3 Commodities

A commodity may be either a service or a good. In the case of a good, one can specify a commodity by listing its physical characteristics. One specifies a service by describing the functions to be performed. Each commodity ought also to have a reference to its location in space; that is, in most applications of the model, a good located at point A should be considered a commodity different from a good with the same physical characteristics located at point B. Commodities may or may not be dated. If commodities are dated, a possible point must be interpreted as a planned set of inputs and outputs for the entire future. With undated commodities a possible point may be either a production plan to be followed for a specified period of time, with the inputs being applied at the beginning of the period and the outputs resulting at the end of the period, or a set of rates of flow for inputs and outputs at any particular point in time.[3]

The exact specification of a commodity depends on the particular application with which one is concerned. For example, the application determines whether commodities need to be located or dated. If we are

[2] Sune Carlson, *A Study of the Pure Theory of Production* (London: P. S. King, 1939), pp. 14–15.

[3] For a more extensive discussion of the definition of commodities, see Debreu, *Theory of Value*, pp. 28–32.

concerned in the theory of the firm with the entrepreneur's plan of production and capital investment over time, then time tags on inputs and outputs are relevant since the value of inputs or outputs at different times in the future must be discounted to obtain present values.[4] The transportation problem,[5] in some cases, requires commodities to be given location tags. In working with the static Leontief input-output model, one is concerned with a production plan where the inputs are applied at the beginning of a period and the outputs resulting at the end of the period.[6] The dynamic Leontief model or the von Neumann model of the expanding economy require that commodities be dated.[7]

## 2.4 Resources and Attainability

A set of production possibilities represents technical know-how without regard to resource limitations; factors are freely variable. This corresponds to the usual conception of the long run. Where there are resource limitations, factors are not freely variable and this situation is usually referred to as the short run. Since our analysis is static and not dynamic, we shall avoid these terms.

DEFINITION 2.4.1. A set of resources is a point $r = (r_1, r_2, \ldots, r_n)$ in Euclidean space.

A set of resources is an a priori given set of commodity amounts which have been inherited from the past. If $r_i$ is positive, it is a resource endowment. If $r_i$ is negative, it is a commodity commitment. A nation's resource endowments, such as capital, may have been produced in the past or, as land or minerals, may have been bestowed upon the population by its environment. A firm's resource endowments are its physical plant and equipment and any services for which the firm may have contracted previously. A nation's commodity commitments encompass various goods and services; for example, it may commit itself to provide medical care for the aged or educational facilities. A firm's commodity commitments are its unfilled orders prior to the period in question. In other words, the set of resources is a set of commodity amounts which are either owned or contracted for use in the case of a resource endowment ($r_i$ positive) or which the economic unit has contracted to provide in the case of a commodity commitment ($r_i$ negative).

Consider a point $z$ which is the sum of a possible point and the set of resources, or $z = r + y$. If $z_i = r_i + y_i$ is positive, it indicates either that

4 On this point see K. E. Boulding, "The Theory of the Firm in the Last Ten Years," *American Economic Review*, Vol. 32 (Dec. 1942), p. 791.

5 See R. Dorfman, P. A. Samuelson, and R. M. Solow, *Linear Programming and Economic Analysis* (New York: McGraw-Hill, 1958), pp. 106–129.

6 *Ibid.*, pp. 204–264.

7 *Ibid.*, pp. 265–308. For a discussion of time and location and their relationship to discounting and transportation costs see Debreu, *Theory of Value*, pp. 29, 33–35.

the $i^{\text{th}}$ resource endowment has not been used to capacity or that more than the $i^{\text{th}}$ commodity commitment has been produced. If $z_i = r_i + y_i$ is negative, it means either that the $i^{\text{th}}$ resource endowment has been used to overcapacity or that the output of the $i^{\text{th}}$ commodity has not satisfied the commodity commitment. Usually we require $z$ to be non-negative. The set of all non-negative $z$ is the attainable set.

DEFINITION 2.4.2. The attainable set is a set $Z$ in Euclidean space such that $z = r + y$ is contained in $Z$ if and only if $z \geqq 0$ and $y$ belongs to $Y$. Any element $z$ belonging to $Z$ is an attainable point.

The attainable set is obtained by translating the set $Y$ of production possibilities, i.e., by shifting the origin to the point $r$, and then taking that part of the translated set which lies in the non-negative quadrant. For example, in Figure 2.2, the set $Y$ is the vertically hatched area. The set $Y$

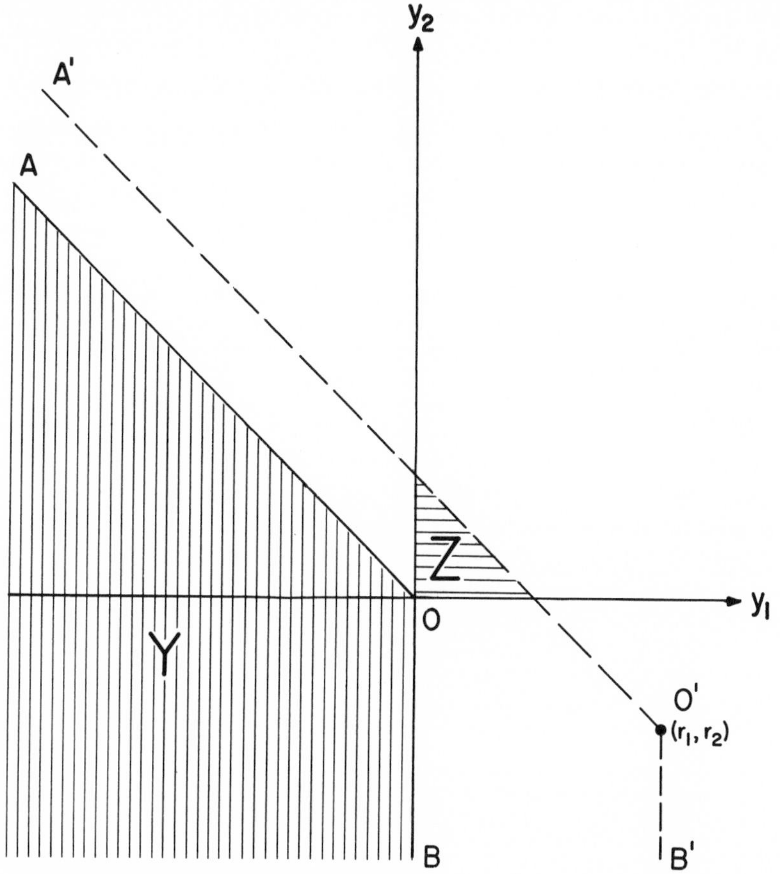


Figure 2.2

is translated so that the origin $O$ becomes the point $O'$ and coincides with the point $r = (r_1, r_2)$. The ray $OA$ is translated to $O'A'$ and the ray $OB$ is translated to $O'B'$. $r_1$ is positive and is a resource endowment. It is a limitation on the amount of commodity 1 which may be used as an input. No more than $r_1$ units of commodity 1 may be used as an input. $r_2$ is negative and is a commodity commitment. At least $r_2$ units of commodity 2 must be produced as an output. The attainable set is the horizontally hatched area and is the intersection of the translated set $Y$ with the non-negative quadrant. In general, the attainable set is that set of points $z = r + y$ where no resource endowment is used to overcapacity and where at least as much as is required is produced as an output for every commodity commitment.

The attainable set takes into account a further limitation introduced on the set of production possibilities. Not every possible point is translatable into an attainable point. The set of possible points which are also attainable is called the set of attainable possible points.

Definition 2.4.3. The set of attainable possible points is the set $\hat{Y}$ containing all possible points $y$ where $z = r + y$ is an attainable point.

The set $\hat{Y}$ is included in the set $Y$ of production possibilities, i.e., $\hat{Y}$ is a subset of $Y$.

## 2.5 Efficiency

The set of production possibilities may admit a very wide range of production plans. The attainable set limits these possibilities to some extent. By introducing a very weak criterion of desirability, one may eliminate a very large proportion of the possible production plans or attainable points from consideration. The weak criterion which we introduce is that of efficiency.

Definition 2.5.1. A possible point $y$ is efficient if and only if there is no other possible point $y'$ where $y' \geq y$, i.e., $y'_i \geqq y_i$ for all $i = 1, \ldots, n$ and $y'_i > y_i$ for at least one $i = 1, \ldots, n$. An attainable point $z$ is efficient if and only if there is no other attainable point $z'$ where $z' \geq z$.

According to this definition a production plan is efficient only if there is no other possible production plan which uses less (in absolute value terms) of at least one commodity as an input or produces more of at least one commodity as an output while using no more (in absolute value terms) of any other commodity as an input and while producing no less of any other commodity as an output.

Efficiency is an invariant property with respect to the set $Y$ of production possibilities and the attainable set $Z$.

Theorem 2.5.1. *If $z = r + y$ is an attainable point, then $z$ is efficient if and only if $y$ is efficient.*

*Proof:* Suppose that $y$ is efficient but that $z$ is not efficient. Then there exists an attainable point $z'$ where $z' \geq z$. If $z' = r + y'$ where $y'$ is possible, then $z' = r + y' \geq z = r + y$ or $y' \geq y$. Thus $y$ is not efficient, which is a contradiction.

Conversely, suppose that $z$ is efficient but that $y$ is not efficient. Then there exists a possible point $y'$ where $y' \geq y$. On the other hand, if $z' = r + y'$, then $z' = r + y' \geq r + y = z$. Since $z$ is attainable, we have $z \geqq 0$. Hence $z' \geq z \geqq 0$ or $z' \geqq 0$ and $z'$ is attainable. Then $z$ is not efficient and we have another contradiction.

Theorem 2.5.1 enables us to conclude that any statement made concerning an efficient attainable point $z = r + y$ is also a statement concerning an efficient possible point $y$. Conversely, any statement concerning an efficient possible point $y$ is also a statement concerning an efficient attainable point $z = r + y$ if in fact $z$ is an attainable point.

In Figure 2.3 the set of production possibilities $Y$ is the shaded area. There are two commodities, one represented by the horizontal axis, the other by the vertical axis. There are no possible points above and to the right of points $y$ and $y'$. Thus they are efficient. The possible point $y'$ lies above and to the right of $y''$, i.e., $y' \geq y''$. Hence $y''$ is not efficient. Suppose the horizontal axis (commodity 1) represents labor hours and the vertical axis (commodity 2) represents shoes. Then $y' = (y'_1, y'_2)$ is a possible point which signifies that an amount $y'_1$ of labor services can be used as an input to produce $y'_2$ shoes. It is not possible to produce more shoes unless more labor hours are used (actually unless $y_2$ is smaller, since $y'_2$ has a negative sign). On the other hand $y'' = (y''_1, y''_2)$ is not efficient because more shoes ($y'_2 > y''_2$) can be produced with fewer labor hours ($y'_1 > y''_1$).

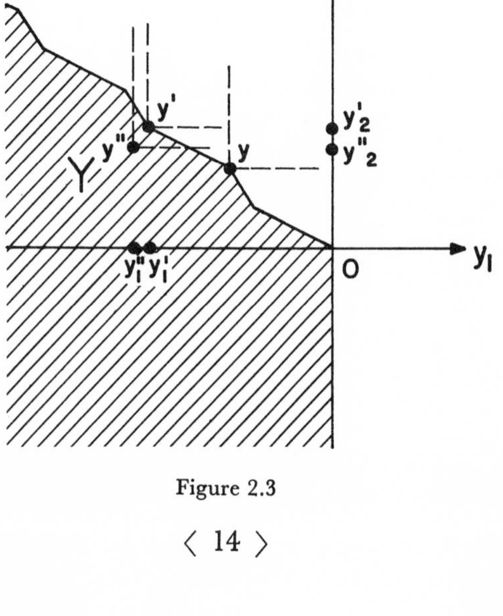


Figure 2.3

## 2.6 Additivity and Inaction

The set of production possibilities $Y$ is assumed throughout to satisfy the following two postulates:

POSTULATE A (*additivity*). If $y'$ and $y''$ are both possible points, then $y' + y''$ is a possible point.

POSTULATE B (*inaction*). $0 = (0, \ldots, 0)$ is a possible point.

Additivity of the production possibilities set means that if two production plans are separately possible, then they are also jointly possible. The total input or output of any commodity in the joint production plan is the algebraic sum of the inputs or outputs of each of the separate production plans.

Let us consider the set of production possibilities open to a firm. It is possible for the firm to double (triple, etc.) the output of all commodities it produces by similarly multiplying all its inputs if the set of production possibilities for that firm satisfies the postulate of additivity. If one plant of a firm can produce $A$ units of a given commodity, then $2A$ units of the commodity can be produced by exactly reproducing the plant facilities. One must remember that the set of production possibilities does not take into account resource limitations. It may be impossible to reproduce a plant because of lack of the same type of land on which to build another plant or lack of managerial talent to run it. The set of production possibilities may still be additive, however, if another plant having the same characteristics is technically feasible given free availability of all resources. Additivity would not hold if despite free availability of resources, it were not possible to reproduce any possible input-output combination without limit. This may occur if some intangible or institutional factor affecting production is not measurable and cannot be classified as an input and doubled or tripled in any meaningful sense.[8]

The set of production possibilities for a firm may not be additive, although the set for an industry may be additive. This would occur if it were not possible for a firm to double (triple, etc.) all outputs with a similar multiplication of all inputs, but free entry into the industry were possible. Suppose one firm is producing $A$ units of an output and another firm can enter the industry and produce exactly the same $A$ units of output by reproducing exactly the first firm's pattern of inputs. Then the industry set of production possibilities would be additive. Additivity for the industry set of production possibilities would not hold if each firm's production possibilities were affected by non-measurable institutional factors which were particular to that firm. Furthermore, if there were

[8] For a discussion of some of the reasons for the absence of additivity see P. A. Samuelson, *Foundations of Economic Analysis* (Cambridge: Harvard University Press, 1963), pp. 81–87.

direct physical interactions among firms, the sum of possible input-output combinations for individual producers might not be possible as a group, that is, there would be external diseconomies. In such a case, additivity would not hold for the industry set of production possibilities. Several other observations about the additivity postulate should be emphasized. First, additivity does not imply constant returns to scale in the usual sense. Additivity implies only that integer increases in scale are *possible.* That is, if $y$ is possible, then $\lambda \cdot y$ is also possible where $\lambda$ is any *positive integer*. Additivity does not rule out the possibility of obtaining more than a doubling (tripling, etc.) of all outputs with a doubling or similar multiplication of all inputs, i.e., increasing returns in some sense may hold. Furthermore, additivity does not imply that $y$ is possible where $\lambda$ is not an integer. Thus in some sense, decreasing returns for certain ranges of scale increases are possible. Finally, an additive set of production possibilities is not equivalent in any sense to a linear homogeneous production function.

The following lemma states that if the postulates of additivity and inaction are satisfied, then the entire ray from the origin through a possible point belongs to the convex hull of $Y$, denoted by $\bar{Y}$.[9]

LEMMA 2.6.1. *Given Postulates A (additivity) and B (inaction), if* $y \in Y$, *then* $\lambda \cdot y \in \bar{Y}$ *where* $\lambda \geqq 0$.

*Proof:* Let $\lambda = [\lambda] + f$ where $[\lambda]$ is the largest integer less than or equal to $\lambda$. The integer $[\lambda]$ is called the integer part of $\lambda$ and the fraction $f$ is called the fractional part of $\lambda$. Given Postulate A, the point $([\lambda] + 1)\, y$ is a possible point since it is a positive integer multiple of the possible point $y$. Let $t = \lambda/([\lambda] + 1)$. Now $0 \leqq t \leqq 1$ and $t \cdot ([\lambda] + 1) \cdot y$ is a convex combination of 0 (inaction )and the possible point $([\lambda] + 1) \cdot y$. Thus $t \cdot ([\lambda] + 1) \cdot y = \lambda y$ is a point in the convex hull $\bar{Y}$ of $Y$.

## 2.7 Disposal

We shall assume that it is possible to dispose of any commodity by using a unit of any commodity as an input without obtaining any other commodity as an output and without using any other commodity as an input.

Let

$$U_j = (u_{1j}, u_{2j}, \ldots, u_{nj})$$

where

$$u_{ij} = 0 \text{ for } i \neq j \text{ and } u_{jj} = -1.$$

$U_j$ is the negative unit vector corresponding to the $j^{\text{th}}$ coordinate.

POSTULATE C (*disposal*). The vectors $U_j$ are contained in $Y$ for $j = 1, \ldots, n$.

[9] For definitions of convex sets and convex hulls see the appendix at the end of the book.

It is therefore possible to dispose of an integer amount of any commodity. Together, Postulate C and Postulate A mean that, given any possible input-output combination, it is possible to produce a *unit* less of any output or it is possible to use a *unit* more (in absolute value terms) of any input, all other inputs and outputs remaining the same.

## 2.8 Closure

At this point we introduce an additional postulate which is difficult to explain in economic terms but necessary to the proof of later theorems.

POSTULATE D (*closure*). The convex hull $\bar{Y}$ of the set $Y$ is closed.

In mathematical terms if we take any sequence of points which approach a given point (come closer and closer to a given point) and the sequence of points is contained in $\bar{Y}$, then the given point must be contained in $\bar{Y}$. For example, if the sequence of points $(1, -1)$, $(\frac{1}{2}, -\frac{1}{3})$, $(\frac{1}{4}, -\frac{1}{6})$, . . . etc., lies in $\bar{Y}$, the point $(0, 0)$ lies in $\bar{Y}$ since the sequence approaches $(0, 0)$.

## 2.9 Properties of the Convex Hull $\bar{Y}$

Postulates A, B, C, and D imply certain things about the convex hull $\bar{Y}$ of the set $Y$ of production possibilities.

THEOREM 2.9.1. *If Postulates A (additivity), B (inaction), and D (closure) are satisfied, the convex hull $\bar{Y}$ of $Y$ is a closed cone.*

*Proof:* Let us define the set $\hat{Y}$ as the set of points $\lambda \cdot y$ where $\lambda \geqq 0$ and $y$ belongs to $Y$. The closure of this set is denoted by $(\hat{Y})$.[10] We shall attempt to show that (*a*) $(\hat{Y})$ is a closed convex cone and (*b*) $(\hat{Y})$ is the convex hull of $Y$.

*Proof that $\hat{Y}$ is a closed convex cone:* The origin 0 belongs to $(\hat{Y})$ by Postulate B. If $a$ is a point of $\hat{Y}$, than $a = \lambda \cdot y$ where $\lambda \geqq 0$ and $y$ is a point of $Y$. Thus $\lambda^0 \cdot a$ belongs to $\hat{Y}$ if $\lambda^0 \geqq 0$ because $\lambda^0 \cdot a = (\lambda^0 \cdot \lambda) \cdot y$ and $\lambda^0 \cdot \lambda \geqq 0$ and $y$ belongs to $\hat{Y}$. Thus $\hat{Y}$ is a cone and therefore its closure $(\hat{Y})$ must be a cone. Now consider any two points $a$ and $b$ which belong to $(\hat{Y})$ such that

(*i*) $a = \lambda^1 \cdot y^1$ and $b = \lambda^2 \cdot y^2$,
(*ii*) $\lambda^1 \geqq 0$ and $\lambda^2 \geqq 0$ are rational scalars, and
(*iii*) $y^1$ and $y^2$ belong to $Y$.

Since $\lambda^1$ and $\lambda^2$ are rational there exists a non-negative integer scalar $\lambda^*$ such that $\lambda^* \cdot \lambda^1$ and $\lambda^* \cdot \lambda^2$ are integers.[11]

[10] For a discussion of the closure of a set, see the appendix.

[11] If $\lambda^1$ and $\lambda^2$ are rational numbers, then each can be expressed as the ratio of integers, i.e.

$$\lambda^1 = \frac{m_1}{n_1}; \qquad \lambda^2 = \frac{m_2}{n_2}.$$

Let $\lambda^* = n_1 \cdot n_2$. Then $\lambda^* \cdot \lambda^1 = n_2 \cdot m_1$, an integer, and $\lambda^* \cdot \lambda^2 = n_1 \cdot m_2$, also an integer.

Thus

$$\lambda^*(a + b) = (\lambda^*\lambda^1)y^1 + (\lambda^* \cdot \lambda^2)y^2$$

is the sum of points belonging to $Y$. Since $(\hat{Y})$ contains the rays of all points belonging to $Y$, the point $(1/\lambda^*) \cdot [\lambda^*(a + b)] = a + b$ belongs to $(\hat{Y})$. For any points $a$ and $b$ of $(\hat{Y})$ which are not of the form given by $(i)$, $(ii)$ and $(iii)$ above, we can find two sequences of points belonging to $(\hat{Y})$ which approach the points $a$ and $b$ and are of this form. The sum of any two points one of which belongs to the sequence approaching $a$ and the other of which belongs to the sequence approaching $b$ forms another sequence, each point of which belongs to $(\hat{Y})$ and which approaches the sum $a + b$. Since $(\hat{Y})$ is closed, the sum $a + b$ belongs to $(\hat{Y})$ and thus $(\hat{Y})$ is a closed convex cone.

*Proof that* $(\hat{Y})$ *is the convex hull of* $Y$*:* The set $(\hat{Y})$ contains all points of $Y$ and is convex. Since $\bar{Y}$ is the smallest convex set containing $Y$, each point of $\bar{Y}$ is a point of $(\hat{Y})$. On the other hand each point of $\hat{Y}$ lies on a ray through a point of $Y$ and thus belongs to the convex hull $\bar{Y}$ (Lemma 2.6.1.). The closure of $\hat{Y}$ must also belong to the convex hull $\bar{Y}$ since $\bar{Y}$ is closed, by Postulate D. Thus each point of $(\hat{Y})$ is a point of $\bar{Y}$. Therefore $(Y)$ and $\bar{Y}$ are the same.

Theorem 2.9.1. figures importantly in this discussion because convex cones have certain known properties. Since $\bar{Y}$ is a convex cone these properties pertain to $\bar{Y}$. The set $Y$ is not necessarily a convex cone. The properties of convex cones must be interpreted differently if $Y$ rather than $\bar{Y}$ is a convex cone.

Figure 2.4 shows four different sets of production possibilities. In Figure 2.4a the set of production possibilities is the set of heavy dots on the dashed line. In Figures 2.4b, 2.4c, and 2.4d, the set of production possibilities is the shaded area.

Figure 2.4a represents an additive set ($Y$ satisfies Postulate A). The point $y$ and all integer multiples of $y$ belong to the set of production possibilities. The set $Y$ in Figure 2.4a does not possess the possibility of inaction (does not satisfy Postulate B) because the origin $(0, 0)$ does not belong to $Y$. Only integer increases in scale are possible for the point $y$. A decrease in scale is impossible. The convex hull $\bar{Y}$ of the set $Y$ is the dashed line in Figure 2.4a.

Figure 2.4b represents a set $Y$ which is both additive and possesses the possibility of inaction, i.e., satisfies both Postulates A and B. Points such as $y$ and $y'$ and all integer multiples of such points are possible points. The half lines emanating from the origin and passing through the points $y$ and $y'$ are scale lines. Any point on the scale line through $y'$ represents an increase in the amount (in absolute value terms) of the input of commodity 1 concomitant with a proportionate increase in the amount of

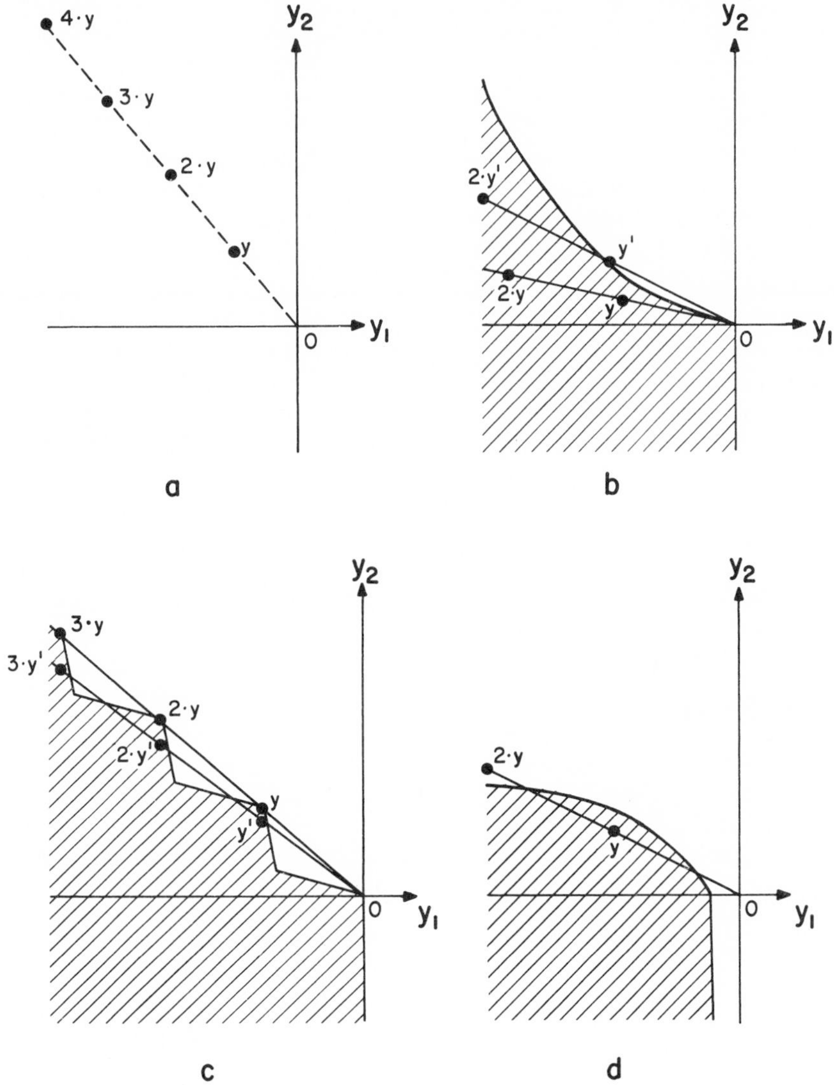


Figure 2.4

output of commodity 2. A decrease in scale of the point $y'$ is not possible except for a decrease in scale to no outputs and no inputs (inaction). This is evidenced by the fact that the part of the scale line between $y'$ and 0 does not lie in the set $Y$. Any increase in scale, however, is possible. In fact, for a given increase (in absolute value terms) of the input of commodity 1, a more than proportionate increase in the output of commodity 2 is possible. This is evidenced by the fact that the part of the scale line beyond $y'$ lies entirely inside the set $Y$.

In Figure 2.4b, the convex hull $\bar{Y}$ of the set $Y$ is not shown. It is the open half-space to the left of the $y_2$ axis including the non-positive part of the $y_2$ axis but not the positive part of the $y_2$ axis. This convex hull is a convex cone as Theorem 2.9.1 indicates.

In Figure 2.4c, the set $Y$ is additive and contains the possibility of inaction. The set $Y$ contains points such as $y$ and $y'$ and all integer multiples of these points. The scale line through $y$ passes through all non-negative integer multiples of $y$. Only integer increases in scale of the point $y$ and a decrease in scale to inaction are possible. For a non-integer change in scale, an increase of the input of commodity 1 results in a less than proportionate increase in output, i.e., for non-integer changes in scale, the only possible points are *below* the scale line. The scale line through $y'$ passes in and out of the set $Y$. For increases in scale of the point $y'$ within certain ranges, a *more* than proportionate increase in output of commodity 2 is possible for a given increase in the input of commodity 1. For increases in scale of the point $y'$ within other ranges, a *less* than proportionate increase in the output of commodity 2 is possible.

In Figure 2.4c, the convex hull $\bar{Y}$ of the set $Y$ is the closed set below the scale line through $y$ and to the left of the $y_2$ axis. This set is a convex cone.

The set $Y$ in Figure 2.4d contains the possibility of inaction, but it is not additive. The set $Y$ is not additive because although the point $y$ belongs to $Y$, the point $2y$ does not belong to $Y$. Any increase in scale of the point $y$ is not possible. A less than proportionate increase in output is possible for a given increase in input. The convex hull $\bar{Y}$ of the set $Y$ is coincident with the set $Y$. That is, the set $Y$ is convex and $\bar{Y} = Y$. The convex hull $\bar{Y}$ is not a convex cone.

The following theorem means that if we are given any point $y$ which is contained in the convex hull $\bar{Y}$ of the set $Y$, then we may add any non-positive vector $w$ to the point $y$ and obtain a point in the convex hull of $Y$.

THEOREM 2.9.2. *Given Postulates A (additivity), B (inaction), C (disposal), and D (closure), if* $y \in \bar{Y}$, *then* $y + w \in \bar{Y}$ *where* $w \leqq 0$.

*Proof:* Any non-positive vector $w$ may be expressed as a weighted sum of the negative unit vectors,

$$w = \sum_{j=1}^{n} \lambda_j \cdot U_j \text{ where } \lambda_j \geqq 0 \text{ for } j = 1, \ldots, n.$$

Since $U_j \in Y$ (Postulate C), according to Lemma 2.6.1, the point $\lambda_j \cdot U_j$ belongs to the convex hull $\bar{Y}$ of the set $Y$ where $\lambda_j \geqq 0$. Theorem 2.9.1 states that $\bar{Y}$ is a convex cone. One of the properties of convex cones is that if $y' \in \bar{Y}$ and $y'' \in \bar{Y}$, then $y' + y'' \in \bar{Y}$. Since

$$y + \sum_{j=1}^{n} \lambda_j \cdot U_j = y + w$$

is a sum of points belonging to $\bar{Y}$, the sum itself belongs to $\bar{Y}$.

In Figure 2.5 the set $Y$ consists of all heavy dots. The shaded area is the convex hull $\bar{Y}$. The set $Y$ satisfies Postulate C (disposal). $Y$ contains the vectors $(-1, 0)$ and $(0, -1)$. The set $Y$ is additive and contains the possibility of inaction. Hence the convex hull $\bar{Y}$ is a convex cone.

Consider any point $y \in Y$ such as $(-2, 2)$ in Figure 2.5. Since $Y$ is additive, we may increase the input of commodity 1 by one unit while the output of commodity 2 remains constant. We obtain the possible point $(-3, 2)$. On the other hand we may reduce the output of commodity 2 by one unit while holding the input of commodity 1 constant. The result is the possible point $(-2, 1)$.

Consider the non-positive point $(-3/2, -1/2)$. If we add this point to the point $(-2,2)$, we obtain $(-7/2, 3/2)$. Now Theorem 2.9.2 implies that the point $(-7/2, 3/2)$ belongs to $\bar{Y}$, the convex hull of $Y$ since $(-3/2, -1/2) \leqq 0$.

## 2.10 Pricing

Definition 2.10.1. A price vector is a point or vector $p = (p_1, p_2, \ldots, p_n)$ in the Euclidean space $E^n$ such that $p \geqq 0$, i.e., $p_i \geqq 0$ for $i = 1, \ldots, n$.

Let us associate with each possible point (with each $y \in Y$), one and only one price vector $p(y)$. In other words let the price vector $p(y)$ be a function of the vector $y \in Y$.

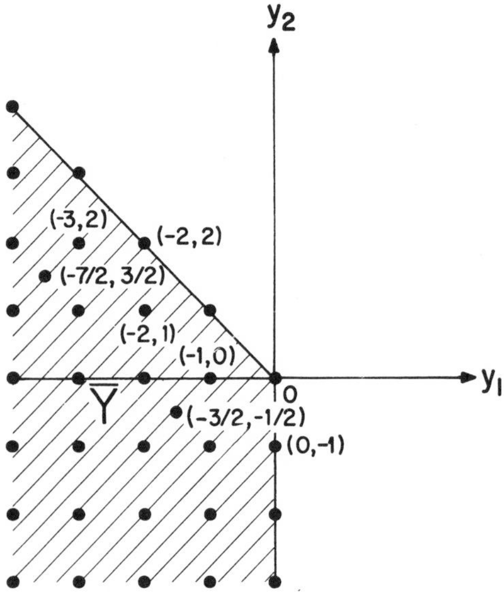


Figure 2.5

DEFINITION 2.10.2. A price system is defined by the function $p(y) = (p_1(y), p_2(y), \ldots, p_n(y))$ which associates one and only one price vector $p(y)$ with each $y \in Y$. If $p(y) = p$ for all $y \in Y$, then the price system is competitive.

If the price vector $p(y)$ varies with the possible point $y$ then the price system is one which is frequently encountered in the theory of monopoly, monopsony, or monopolistic competition. That is, the price of a commodity varies with the input or output of that commodity. The price of a particular commodity may also vary with the input and output of other commodities.

Suppose there is only one price vector $p$ associated with all $y \in Y$. Then we have a competitive price system. If any decision maker is faced with such a price system, he must take prices as a set of parameters given to him. At times, we shall refer to a competitive price system as a parametric price system or as a system of parametric prices.

If the *vector* $p(y)$ varies with the *vector* $y$, then the price of any particular commodity, say the $j^{\text{th}}$ commodity, may be dependent on the amount of other commodities $i$ for $i \neq j$ as well as the amount of the $j^{\text{th}}$ commodity. If the price of a commodity varies *only* with the amount of that particular commodity, then the price system is independent. In this case the *co-ordinate* $p_i$ varies with the *co-ordinate* $y_i$. Let $p_i(y_i)$ be a scalar quantity, a price, which is a function of the scalar $y_i$, the amount of the $i^{\text{th}}$ commodity.

DEFINITION 2.10.3. If $p(y) = (p_1(y_1), p_2(y_2), \ldots, p_n(y_n))$ then the price system $p(y)$ is independent.

Suppose we have an independent price system such that the price $p_i(y_i)$ does not rise as the amount of the $i^{\text{th}}$ commodity increases. This means that if $y_i$ is an output, as more of the output is obtained, the price of the output does not rise. It may fall, of course. This also means that if $y_i$ is an input and $y_i$ increases (the absolute value of $y_i$ decreases), the price of the input does not rise. More precisely, we define such a price system as follows:

DEFINITION 2.10.4. An inverse price system is an independent price system $p(y)$ which is such that $y_i^* \geqq y_i$ implies that $p_i(y_i^*) \leqq p_i(y_i)$.

An inverse system is one which has an inverse relationship between prices and quantities. This corresponds to a falling demand curve for outputs or a rising supply curve for inputs.

One other special type of price system with which we shall be concerned is one where a proportionate increase in all inputs and outputs leaves prices invariant.

DEFINITION 2.10.5. If $\lambda \cdot y \in Y$, where $\lambda \geqq 0$, then a price system $p(y)$ such that $p(\lambda \cdot y) = p(y)$ is homogeneous of degree zero.

A competitive price system is always homogeneous of degree zero since there is only one set of prices which remains invariant for all possible production combinations.

We can illustrate an inverse price system with the aid of Figure 2.6. On the horizontal axis we have the amount $y_i$ of the $i^{th}$ commodity. The vertical axis represents the price of the $i^{th}$ commodity. If the function $p_i(y_i)$ is continuous then an inverse price system is such that $p_i(y_i)$ has a non-positive slope. To go in the positive direction on the $y_i$ axis is either to use less (in absolute value) of the $i^{th}$ commodity as an input or to produce more of the $i^{th}$ commodity as an output. Price does not rise (but may fall) as we go in a positive direction on the $y_i$ axis.

Our concept of an inverse price system is similar to the notion that all demand curves are falling and all supply curves are rising. In making this analogy two things ought to be kept in mind. One is that a commodity is allowed to be both an input and an output. Hence the amount of that commodity may be positive or negative. The function $p_i(y_i)$ is, so to speak, both a demand curve and a supply curve depending on whether $y_i$ is positive or negative. Second, we have in no way implied that the function $p_i(y_i)$ is either continuous or defined for all real numbers. For example, the function $p_i(y_i)$ may be defined only for integer $y_i$. Thus the graph of the function $p_i(y_i)$ in Figure 2.6 represents only a special case.

A note of caution is in order as regards any attempt to make an analogy between the functions $p_i(y_i)$ of an independent price system and supply or demand curves. These functions are taken as given and have

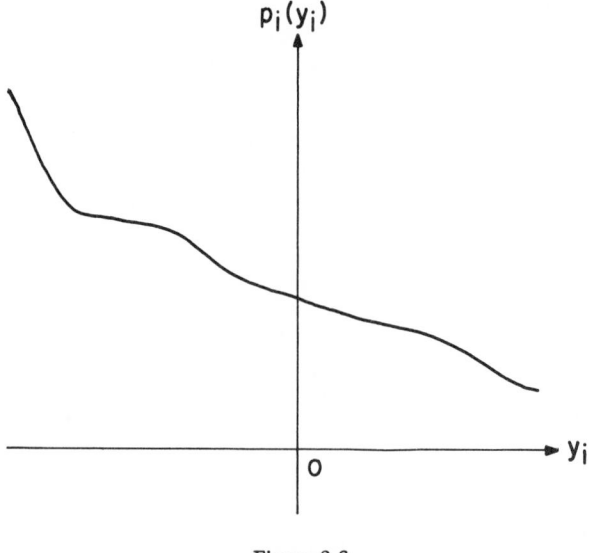

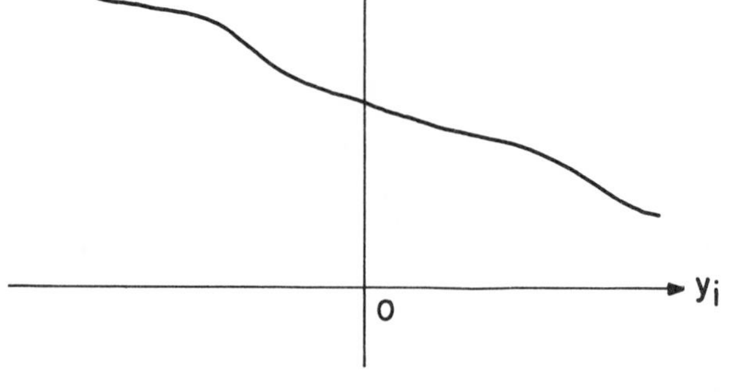


Figure 2.6

not been derived by consumer utility or producer cost considerations. The functions $p_i(y_i)$ may be considered to be price-quantity relationships imposed by fiat.

## 2.11 Profit Maximization

We define the profit of a possible point $y$ or of an attainable point $z$ as follows:

DEFINITION 2.11.1. The profit of a possible point $y$ is the product[12] $\pi(y) = p(y) \cdot y$. The profit of an attainable point $z$ is the product $\pi(z) = p(y) \cdot z = p(y) \cdot y + p(y) \cdot r$.

$$\pi(y) = p_1(y) \cdot y_1 + p_2(y) \cdot y_2 + \cdots + p_n(y) \cdot y_n = \sum_{i=1}^{n} p_i(y) \cdot y_i$$

$$\pi(z) = \sum_{i=1}^{n} p_i(y) \cdot y_i + \sum_{i=1}^{n} p_i(y) \cdot r_i = \sum_{i=1}^{n} p_i(y) \cdot (y_i + r_i)$$

Note that outputs have positive co-ordinates and inputs have negative co-ordinates. Thus, $p_i(y) \cdot y_i$ is positive when the $i^{\text{th}}$ co-ordinate is an output. Hence, our definition of the profit of a possible point is the traditional one of revenues less costs, if we call a positive term a revenue and the absolute value of a negative term a cost.

Each possible input-output combination $y$ and each attainable point has an assigned value—its profits.

DEFINITION 2.11.2. Given a price system $p(y)$, a profit-maximizing possible point is a point $y^* \in Y$ such that $p(y^*) \cdot y^* \geqq p(y) \cdot y$ for all $y \in Y$. A profit-maximizing attainable point is a point $z^* \in Z$ such that $\pi(z^*) \geqq \pi(z)$ for all $z \in Z$.

There may be more than one profit-maximizing possible input-output combination $y$ according to this definition. As a matter of convenience, we shall at times refer to a point as profit-maximizing, but it is understood that we mean the point is a profit-maximizing *possible* point.

Suppose we have a competitive system of prices $p(y) = p$ for all $y \in Y$. The price vector $p$ may be any one of the price vectors lying in the non-negative orthant of $E^n$. The following theorem allows us either to consider only a subset of all the possible price vectors in the non-negative orthant or to consider $n - 1$ prices rather than all $n$ prices $p_1, \ldots, p_n$.

THEOREM 2.11.1. *If $y^*$ is profit-maximizing for the competitive price system $p(y) = p$ then $y^*$ is profit-maximizing for the price system $p(y) = \lambda \cdot p$ for all $y \in Y$ where $\lambda > 0$.*

*Proof:* Since $p \cdot y^* \geqq p \cdot y$ for all $y \in Y$, $\lambda \cdot p \cdot y^* \geqq \lambda \cdot p \cdot y$ for all $y \in Y$ if $\lambda > 0$.

[12] See appendix for the definition of the product of two vectors.

The fact that the set of profit-maximizing points remains invariant under scalar multiplication of the price vector $p$ means that we may choose one desired commodity as a *numeraire* and set its price equal to unity. Alternatively, we may normalize the price vector $p$ by requiring $\sum_{i=1}^{n} p_i = 1$. All possible price vectors would then lie in the non-negative orthant of the Euclidean space and also in the hyperplane $\sum_{i=1}^{n} p_i = 1$.

One of the conditions of the theorem below is that the price system be homogeneous of degree zero, i.e., $p(\lambda \cdot y) = p(y)$.

THEOREM 2.11.2. *If the set $Y$ satisfies Postulates A (additivity) and B (inaction) and if the price system $p(y)$ is homogeneous of degree zero, then maximum profits are zero if a profit-maximizing point $y^*$ exists.*

*Proof:* Maximum profits cannot be negative since $0 \in Y$ (inaction) and $p(0) \cdot 0 = 0$. Suppose $y^*$ is profit-maximizing and $p(y^*) \cdot y^* > 0$. Now $k \cdot y^* \in Y$ where $k \geqq 2$ and $k$ is integer (additivity), and $p(k \cdot y^*) = p(y^*)$ because the price system is homogeneous of degree zero. Thus, we have $p(k \cdot y^*) \cdot (k \cdot y^*) = p(y^*) \cdot k(y^*) > p(y^*) \cdot y^*$.

The above shows that if the manager of a firm with an additive production possibilities set has a profitable operation, he can increase his profits by continually expanding his operations so long as there are available resources. If an industry has an additive production set (if there is free entry), then so long as there are positive profits, firms can profitably enter the industry. The only check on the expansion of the firm or the number of firms in the industry is the limit of available resources. Only when profits are zero can firms be induced to limit their scale of operations or will firms be discouraged from entering the industry.

There is a corollary which follows from Theorem 2.11.2 and which asserts essentially that if a profit-maximizing point $y^*$ exists, the manager of a firm with an additive set of production possibilities cannot increase or decrease his profits by multiplying his scale of operations or by decreasing his scale of operations if it is possible to do so.

COROLLARY 2.11.2. *Given Postulates A and B and that the price system $p(y)$ is homogeneous of degree zero, if $y^*$ is profit-maximizing and if $\lambda \cdot y^* \in Y$, then $\lambda \cdot y^*$ is profit-maximizing.*

*Proof:* Theorem 2.11.2 states that $p(y^*) \cdot y^* = 0$. Since $p(\lambda \cdot y^*) = p(y^*)$, we have $p(\lambda \cdot y^*) \cdot \lambda \cdot y^* = \lambda(p(y^*) \cdot y^*) = 0$.

For any profit maximizing point $y^*$, therefore, all possible points lying on a ray through the point $y^*$ are profit-maximizing. This corollary, of course, depends on the homogeneity of degree zero of the price system.

Let us consider two separate competitive price systems $p$ and $p'$. The following theorem is familiar and concerns price variations.

THEOREM 2.11.3. *If $y$ is a profit-maximizing possible point or if $z = r + y$ is a profit-maximizing attainable point for the competitive price system $p(y) = p$ for all $y \in Y$, and if $y'$ is a profit-maximizing possible point or if $z' = r + y'$ is a profit-maximizing attainable point for the competitive price system $p(y) = p'$ for all $y \in Y$, then $(p' - p)\cdot(y' - y) \geqq 0$.*

*Proof:* By definition, $p\cdot y \geqq p\cdot y'$ $(p\cdot y + p\cdot r \geqq p\cdot y' + p\cdot r)$ if $y(z = r + y)$ is a profit-maximizing possible (attainable) point. If we subtract $p\cdot y'(p\cdot y' + p\cdot r)$ from both sides of this inequality, we obtain the inequality $-p\cdot(y' - y) \geqq 0$. Also by definition $p'\cdot y' \geqq p'\cdot y(p'\cdot y' + p'\cdot r \geqq p'\cdot y + p'\cdot r)$. If we subtract $p'\cdot y(p'\cdot y + p'\cdot r)$ from both sides of this inequality we obtain the inequality $p'\cdot(y' - y) \geqq 0$. Adding these two derived inequalities, we obtain $(p' - p)\cdot(y' - y) \geqq 0$.

If we consider a change in only one price, say $p_j' - p_j > 0$ and $p_i' - p_i = 0$ for $i \neq j$, then Theorem 2.11.3 states that $y_j' - y_j \geqq 0$, i.e., an increase in the price of the $j^{\text{th}}$ commodity, all other prices being held constant, results in no decrease of the $j^{\text{th}}$ commodity being produced if the $j^{\text{th}}$ commodity is an output or results in no increase (in absolute value terms) in the use of the $j^{\text{th}}$ commodity if the $j^{\text{th}}$ commodity is an input. Alternatively, if the price of the $j^{\text{th}}$ commodity is reduced, i.e., $p_j' - p_j < 0$ and $p_i' - p_i = 0$ for $i \neq j$, then $y_j' - y_j \leqq 0$. This means that the $j^{\text{th}}$ output is not increased or the $j^{\text{th}}$ input is not decreased.

In Figure 2.7, the set $Y$ of production possibilities is the shaded area not including the ray from the origin through $y$ and $2y$. The only points on the ray through $y$ and $2y$ which belong to $Y$ and $y$ are non-negative integer multiples of $y$. The set $Y$ is additive and contains the possibility of

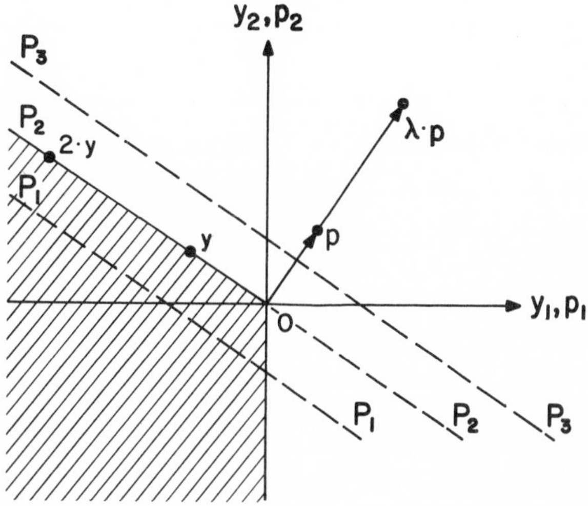


Figure 2.7

inaction. The horizontal axis represents either the amount $y_1$ of commodity 1 or the price $p_1$. The vertical axis represents either the amount $y_2$ of commodity 2 or the price $p_2$. The point $p$ represents a price vector. It lies in the non-negative quadrant of the two-dimensional Euclidean space which is pictured in Figure 2.7.

The hyperplane $P_2P_2$ (or line) in Figure 2.7 is perpendicular to the price vector $p$. All points on the line $P_2P_2$ (which is called an iso-profit line) represent points of equal profit. Any hyperplane parallel to $P_2P_2$, such as $P_1P_1$ or $P_3P_3$, is also an iso-profit line. The line $P_1P_1$ represents negative profit, the line $P_2P_2$ represents zero profit, and the line $P_3P_3$ represents positive profit. If $p(y) = p$ is a competitive system of prices, the point $y$ and integer multiples of $y$ are profit-maximizing and give zero profits. For $\lambda$ not an integer, $\lambda \cdot y$ is not a possible point. Therefore, if and only if $\lambda$ is an integer, $\lambda \cdot y$ is profit-maximizing. For a competitive system of prices $p(y) = \lambda \cdot p$, where $\lambda$ is any positive scalar, the set of profit-maximizing points remains invariant with respect to $\lambda$.

In Figure 2.8 the horizontal axis represents either the amount $y_1$ of commodity 1 or the price $p_1$ of commodity 1 and the vertical axis represents either the amount $y_2$ of commodity 2 or the price $p_2$ of commodity 2. The three competitive price systems $p(y) = p$, $p(y) = p'$, and $p(y) = p''$ can all be represented as price vectors which lie on the line $p_1 + p_2 = 1$. In other words, the three price vectors $p$, $p'$, and $p''$ are normalized.

The set of production possibilities $Y$ is the shaded area in Figure 2.8. This set is additive and contains the possibility of inaction. For the competitive price system $p(y) = p$ all points which lie on the ray through $y$

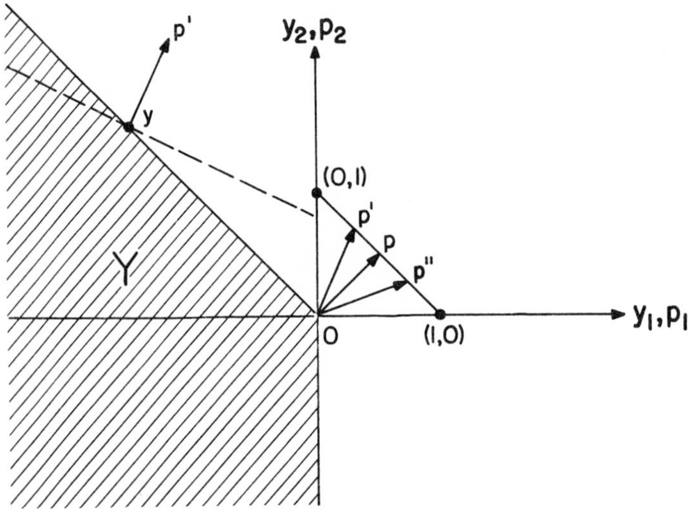


Figure 2.8

are profit-maximizing points. Maximum profits are zero. For the competitive price system $p(y) = p''$, there is only one profit-maximizing point, 0 or inaction. Again maximum profits are zero. Any possible point other than 0 gives a negative profit. For the competitive price system $p(y) = p'$, there are no profit maximizing points. The point $y$ gives positive profits and any integer multiple of $y$ can give even greater profits—profits are unlimited.

The price vectors $p = (p_1, p_2)$ and $p'' = (p_1'', p_2'')$ in Figure 2.8 are such that $p_1'' > p_1$ and $p_2'' < p_2$. The point $y$ is profit-maximizing for the competitive system $p(y) = p$ and 0 is profit-maximizing for the competitive system $p(y) = p''$. The point $y = (y_1, y_2)$ is such that $y_2 > 0$ and $y_1 < 0$ (commodity 2 is an output and commodity 1 is an input). Now $(p_1'' - p_1)\cdot(0 - y_1) > 0$. That is, an increase in price from $p_1$ to $p_1''$ increases the amount of commodity 1 (reduces in absolute value the amount of commodity 1 as an input). Similarly $(p_2'' - p_2)\cdot(0 - y_2) > 0$. A reduction in price from $p_2$ to $p_2''$ reduces the output of commodity 2.

## 2.12 Pricing and Efficiency

We now prove the efficiency theorem, which provides a link between the two criteria of desirability—profit maximization and efficiency—under a competitive price system.

THEOREM 2.12.1. (*efficiency*). *If there exists a competitive price system $p(y) = p > 0$ for all $y \in Y$ such that $y^*$ is a profit-maximizing possible point or $z^* = r + y^*$ is a profit-maximizing attainable point, then $y^*$ is efficient or $z^*$ is efficient.*

*Proof:* Suppose $y^*$ $(z^* = y^* + r)$ is profit-maximizing but is not efficient. Then there exists some $y^{**} \in Y$ $(z^{**} \in Z)$ such that $y^{**} \geq y^*$ $(z^{**} \geq z^*)$. Now $p\cdot y^{**} - p\cdot y^* = p\cdot(y^{**} - y^*)$ $(p\cdot z^{**} - p\cdot z^* = p\cdot(z^{**} - z^*))$. Since $p > 0$ and $(y^{**} - y^*) \geq 0$ $((z^{**} - z^*) \geq 0)$, we have $p\cdot(y^{**} - y^*) > 0$ $(p\cdot(z^{**} - z^*) > 0)$. Then $p\cdot y^{**} > p\cdot y^*$ $(p\cdot z^{**} > p\cdot z^*)$ and $y^*$ $(z^*)$ cannot be profit-maximizing, which is a contradiction.

Note that Theorem 2.12.1 requires that the price vector $p$ be positive, i.e., $p_i > 0$ for all $i$. If we can prove that for each efficient point $y^*$ there is a price vector $p > 0$ such that $y^*$ is profit-maximizing then we have proved the converse of this theorem. It is the converse of Theorem 2.12.1 that is important for the theory of decentralized decision making. Postulates A, B, C and D are not sufficient in order that the converse of Theorem 2.12.1 should hold.

Figure 2.9 illustrates a set $Y$ of production possibilities. The set $Y$ is the shaded area. The point $y$ is profit-maximizing for the competitive price system $p(y) = p$. The point $y$ is also efficient. Otherwise there would

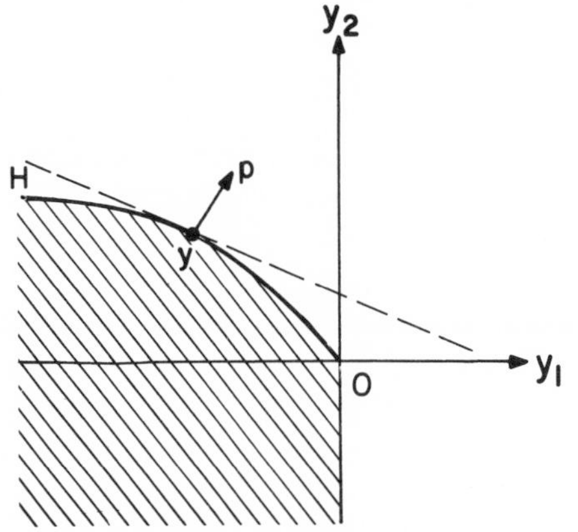


Figure 2.9

be a possible point above and to the right of $y$ which would give a higher profit. The line $H$ is a supporting hyperplane. Any point which lies above and to the right of the line $H$ is not a possible point.

## 2.13 The Missing Postulate

So far in this chapter we have omitted a postulate of divisibility. Divisibility may be stated as follows: if $y$ is a possible point, then $\lambda \cdot y$ is also a possible point, where $\lambda$ is any positive scalar. The assumption of divisibility means that there are possible points which have fractional units of inputs and outputs. Postulates A and B, together with a postulate of divisibility, imply that the set of production possibilities is a convex cone with vertex the origin. Since convex cones have certain known desirable properties, these postulates make it possible to prove some useful theorems about production sets. A postulate of divisibility also means that there are constant returns to scale according to the usual definitions of returns to scale. We do not use a divisibility postulate in our analysis but will provide a substitute. Production sets under this alternative hypothesis do not possess constant returns to scale.

The divisibility postulate and Postulates A and B would enable us to prove the converse of Theorem 2.12.1. That is, for each efficient point $y^*$ we could determine a competitive system of prices which would make $y^*$ a profit-maximizing point.

## 2.14 Conclusions

In this chapter we have presented four postulates: A (additivity), B (inaction), C (disposal) and D (closure). Postulate A is perhaps the most controversial, especially if the set $Y$ of production possibilities refers to the firm rather than the industry. One of the frequently cited reasons for the firm's lack of ability to increase its scale of operations without limit is the fact that there are "problems of co-ordination arising from increasing complexity."[13] Although it may be possible for an industry to increase its scale of operations without limit (provided, of course, that there are no resource limitations), if a single firm tries to conduct the operations of a whole industry, "co-ordination which formerly took place through buying and selling to each other now takes place internally."[14] Certain goods are not priced, because they no longer enter the market. These goods which were formerly allocated among different firms through a market mechanism now must be allocated internally. A cost may be involved in setting up the system of internal allocation, that is, there may be increased difficulties of coordination. Insofar as we regard a firm as a decision-making unit, production decisions and coordination must be directed by one "brain," and the major difficulty is the obtaining of all relevant information by the "brain" in order to make decisions within the required amount of time. Therefore, it becomes a question of the pure impossibility of production beyond a certain scale by a single decision unit.[15] Unless there is some coordination between various parts of a business enterprise, a "firm" as any sort of entity, defined or undefined, loses its significance.

Other reasons given in the literature explain why the scale of the firm cannot increase without limit. Reder postulates that the owner's fear of loss of control is the major factor in limiting the size of the firm.[16] Kalecki advances the "principle of increasing risk," which keeps firms from expanding. As a firm expands, the entrepreneur must borrow more capital, so that for a given percentage loss of invested capital, a greater percentage of his own capital will be lost.[17]

For these reasons, the set $Y$ can more reasonably refer to an industry than to a firm. In the industry case, additivity (Postulate A) implies free entry.

Variations of Theorems 2.11.3 have an interesting history. It is very similar to the traditional theorem that the substitution effect is negative.[18]

[13] E. H. Chamberlin, *The Theory of Monopolistic Competition*, p. 247.

[14] Richard B. Heflebower, "Economics of Size," *Journal of Business* (University of Chicago), Vol. 24 (Oct. 1951), p. 253.

[15] N. Kaldor, "The Equilibrium of the Firm," *Economic Journal*, Vol. 44 (March 1934), p. 69.

[16] Melvin W. Reder, "A Reconsideration of the Marginal Productivity Theory," *Journal of Political Economy*, Vol. 55 (Oct. 1947), p. 450.

[17] M. Kalecki, *Essays in the Theory of Economic Fluctuations* (New York: Farrar and Rinehart, Inc., 1939), pp. 95–107. We have excluded any arguments concerning the limitation of firm size which are based on the limited availability of certain resources such as managerial talent or on a downward sloping demand curve, since we are concerned only with the technical possibilities of which an owner of a firm can or desires to take advantage, disregarding factor limitations or market conditions.

[18] See Kenneth E. Boulding, *Economic Analysis* (1st edn. New York: Harper, 1941), pp. 510, 519–520. Also see Sune Carlson, *A Study of the Pure Theory of Production*, pp. 32–33.

The substitution effect, however, pertains to cost minimization with a given output. The usual argument is that a diminishing marginal rate of substitution (along an isoquant) implies that an increase in the price of one input, with prices of other inputs constant, results in less of that input being used.

Samuelson[19] shows that if there are discontinuities in the isoquant, the substitution effect is non-positive; an increase in the price of an input results in either less of the input being used or no change in the amount of the input. Samuelson's theorem is slightly more general in that a continuously diminishing marginal rate of substitution is not necessary for his results. He does assume, however, that except for points of discontinuity, marginal rates of substitution are non-increasing.

Our Theorem 2.11.3 does not require any assumptions about marginal rates of substitution.[20] It is stated in terms of profit maximization rather than cost minimization. We can, however, consider only a subset of $Y$, namely, the set of all possible points corresponding to a given level of output for the $i^{\text{th}}$ commodity. Profit maximization over this subset is equivalent to a minimization of costs, provided all other commodities are inputs. The proof of Theorem 2.11.3 carries through in exactly the same way if cost minimization is defined over this subset of $Y$. Thus Theorem 2.11.3 can be reduced as a special case to a demonstration that the substitution effect is non-positive. Instead of assuming a non-increasing marginal rate of substitution we assume that a cost-minimizing set of inputs exists. The rest of the proof depends entirely on the definitions of prices and cost minimization.

All of the theorems in this chapter were proved without the aid of the divisibility postulate. These theorems constitute a body of theory which is independent of whether commodities are divisible.

[19] Paul A. Samuelson, *Foundations of Economic Analysis* (Cambridge: Harvard University Press, 1947), pp. 80–81.

[20] The proof of Theorem 2.11.3 in this volume is similar to that of Debreu, *Theory of Value*, p. 47.

# CHAPTER 3

# *INDIVISIBLE COMMODITIES AND RETURNS TO SCALE*

## 3.1 Introduction

In this chapter we discuss and precisely define an *indivisible commodity*. Then we introduce additional assumptions, *integer convexity* and *joint use and joint production*, concerning the set $Y$ of production possibilities. Two other important concepts are discussed—those of *increasing returns* and *constant returns* for integer changes in scale.

## 3.2 The Meaning of an Indivisible Commodity

Formally, we define an indivisible commodity as follows:

Definition 3.2.1. The commodity represented by the $i^{\text{th}}$ co-ordinate in the Euclidean space $E^n$ is an indivisible commodity if for all $y$ contained in $Y$, $y_i$ is integer.

In concrete situations one might want to specify that certain commodities are indivisible in several different circumstances: (*a*) where a given amount of a commodity cannot be physically divided into fractional parts in any meaningful sense; (*b*) when fractional parts of a commodity cannot be physically combined in a meaningful sense; (*c*) when for any reason, institutional or otherwise, a decision unit cannot purchase fractional parts of an input; and (*d*) when for any reason a decision unit cannot sell fractional parts of an output.

Let us consider some real-life examples of situations where these phenomena are present. An industrial heat exchanger with a two-million-ton capacity can be cut into two piles of steel scrap and other debris, but the two piles of scrap can in no way be described as two heat exchangers with a capacity of a million tons apiece. A one-carat diamond can be cut into two half-carat diamonds, but modern technology has not as yet devised a way to put the two halves of the diamond together again. Here division is not reversible. For certain purposes one might want to regard heat exchangers and diamonds as indivisible commodities.

Purchase of fractional amounts of inputs may be impossible in many different situations. Suppose a truck rental firm rents trucks on a per week basis. A customer of the truck rental firm may desire to use truck services for only part of a week. If the truck rental firm and all other available truck rental firms refuse to rent trucks on less than a week's terms (whatever the reason), then as far as the client is concerned, truck services may have to be regarded as an indivisible input.

As another example, let us consider managerial services. Individual managers, except those of the management consultant sort, must usually be hired full time or not at all by any particular corporation or firm. Even if two firms were willing to share the services of one manager so that each could hire him part time, the physical location of the manager may be so important that it might be impractical or impossible for him to manage two operations at once.

Consider also labor services of any sort. Individuals and groups of individuals may be hired only under contract for a certain specified time. Such contracts may be legally enforced, enforced by custom, or enforced by previous bargaining arrangements. For example, a guaranteed annual wage is usually a bargaining arrangement whereby a firm must buy labor services in one-year units.

Decision units are often not able to sell fractional units of a commodity. Cornflakes come in small, large, and giant size boxes and in no other way. Automobiles are compact, medium sized, or monster sized. Even if product sizes are an open question, in some instances a limited number of discrete sizes may be taken as given from the result of previous optimizing decisions. In other words, a firm or group of firms in an industry may find that certain savings will accrue if product sizes are standardized and select a few standard sizes to produce. These standard size products might then be regarded as indivisible.[1]

Let $I$ be a set of indices $i = 1, \ldots, n$ each one corresponding to a different co-ordinate in the $n$-dimensional space $E^n$. Then $I$ can be partitioned into two sets $D$ and $D^*$. The $i$ belonging to $D$ represent indivisible commodities. All other commodities, represented by those $i$ in $D^*$, are called divisible commodities. The reason we call all non-indivisible commodities divisible will become clear later when we introduce the postulate of integer convexity. We call a commodity indivisible when and only when that commodity can be represented by integers. This does not take into account commodities which can be bought or sold only in amounts greater than some critical amount. Nor does it consider commodities which can only be represented by certain intervals on the line of real numbers. For example, the variable $y_i$ may be defined as a commodity amount only for $\frac{1}{2} \leqq y_i \leqq 1$, $\frac{4}{3} \leqq y_i \leqq 2$, $\frac{9}{4} \leqq y_i \leqq 3$, etc. We shall not be concerned with such representations of commodity amounts.

### 3.3 Integer Convexity

Obviously, a production set $Y$ which contains indivisible commodities cannot be convex. That is, if $y'$ belongs to $Y$ and $y''$ belongs to $Y$, then $y = \lambda \cdot y' + (1 - \lambda) \cdot y''$ for $0 \leqq \lambda \leqq 1$ is not necessarily contained in $Y$.

[1] For a discussion of the problem of choosing an optimal set of standardized product sizes see C. R. Frank, Jr., "A Note on the Assortment Problem," *Management Science*, Vol. II (May 1965), 724–726.

The reason is that if $i$ is in $D$, then $y_i = \lambda \cdot y_i' + (1 - \lambda)y_i''$ is not necessarily integer for some values of $\lambda$. Thus according to Definition 3.2.1 of an indivisible commodity, for certain values of $\lambda$, $y$ is not a possible point.

Since convexity (as normally defined) and indivisible commodities are incompatible concepts, we should like to find a generalization of the notion of convexity that is compatible with the existence of indivisible commodities. For this purpose we shall not speak of convexity in the traditional sense of the word, but shall concern ourselves with a generalization called integer convexity. Suppose $y$ belongs to $\bar{Y}$, the convex hull of the set $Y$. If $y$ belongs to $Y$ as well as $\bar{Y}$, then the $i^{\text{th}}$ co-ordinate $y_i$ must be integer if $i$ is in $D$, i.e., if the $i^{\text{th}}$ commodity is indivisible. Integer convexity requires that if $y$ is contained in $\bar{Y}$, and the $i^{\text{th}}$ co-ordinate $y_i$ is integer for all $i$ in $D$, then $y$ is contained in $Y$ as well.

Definition 3.3.1. A set $Y$ is integer convex if, whenever $y$ belongs to $\bar{Y}$ and $y_i$ is integer for all $i$ in $D$, then $y$ belongs to $Y$.

If the set $Y$ of production possibilities is integer convex, then it satisfies.

Postulate E (*integer convexity*). The set $Y$ of production possibilities is integer convex.

## 3.4 Geometric Interpretation of Integer Convexity

Integer convexity is here illustrated by example. Figure 3.1 shows an integer convex set $Y$ of production possibilities. There are two commodities, the amount $y_1$ of commodity 1 represented by the horizontal axis and the amount $y_2$ of commodity 2 represented by the vertical axis. The convex hull $\bar{Y}$ of the set $Y$ is the shaded area. Both commodities 1 and 2 are indivisible. According to the postulate of integer convexity, the set $Y$ itself consists of all points in the convex hull $\bar{Y}$ of the set $Y$ which have integer co-ordinates. The points of $Y$ are represented by the heavy dots in Figure 3.1.

Figure 3.2 shows another integer convex set $Y$ where there are two commodities. The convex hull $Y$ is the shaded area. In this case, however, commodity 1 is divisible and commodity 2 is indivisible. The set $Y$ itself consists of all points $(y_1, y_2)$ where $y_2$, the amount of commodity 2 (measured on the vertical axis) is integer and where point $(y_1, y_2)$ lies in the convex hull $\bar{Y}$. Since commodity 1 is divisible, the amount $y_1$ of commodity 1 need not be integer. Only $y_2$ is required to be integer. The set $Y$ consists of all points on the heavy lines parallel to the $y_1$ axis and lying in the convex hull $\bar{Y}$.

Figure 3.3 is an attempt to represent an integer convex set $Y$ where there are three commodities. Commodities 1 and 2 are divisible while commodity 3 is indivisible. The convex hull $\bar{Y}$ of the set $Y$ is the convex

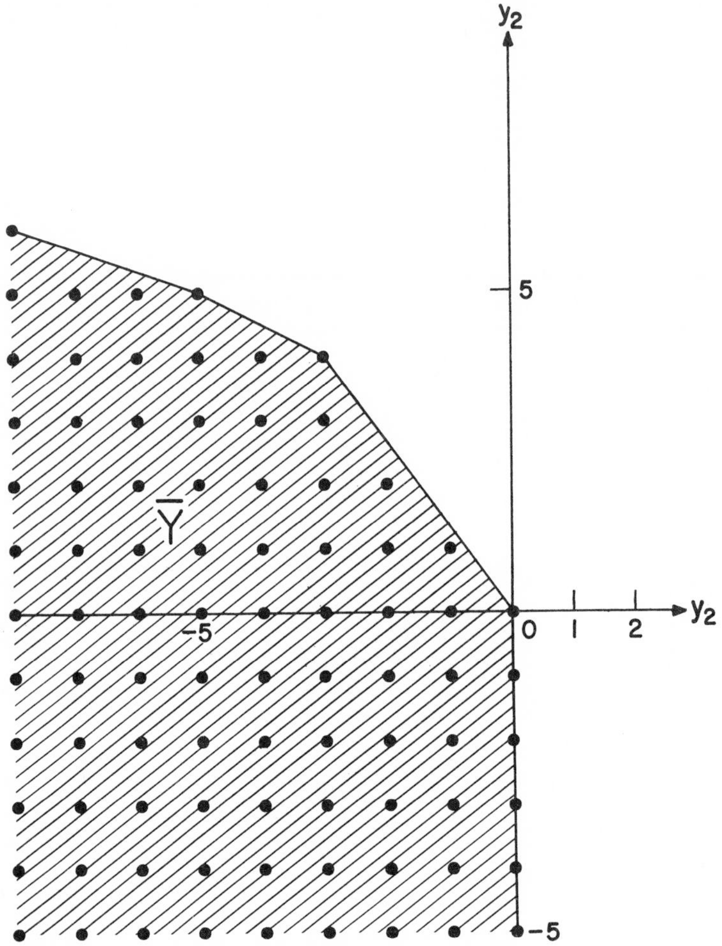


Figure 3.1

cone formed by the four rays: $OA$, $OB$, $OC$, and $OD$. The set $Y$ consists of all points lying in this cone where the amount $y_3$ of commodity 3 is integer but where $y_1$ and $y_2$ are not necessarily integer. In geometric terms, the set $Y$ consists of a series of unbounded polyhedrons which are parallel to the $y_1$, $y_2$ plane, set one unit apart along the $y_3$ axis, and are entirely contained in the convex hull $\bar{Y}$. Two of these polyhedrons are represented in Figure 3.3. The one has vertices at $(0, 0, -1)$, $E$ and $F$. The other has vertices at $(0, 0, -2)$, $G$ and $H$.

### 3.5 Joint Use and Joint Production

Given any vector $y$, if brackets are placed around the vector the resulting vector $[y]$ is the largest integer vector which is less than or equal to

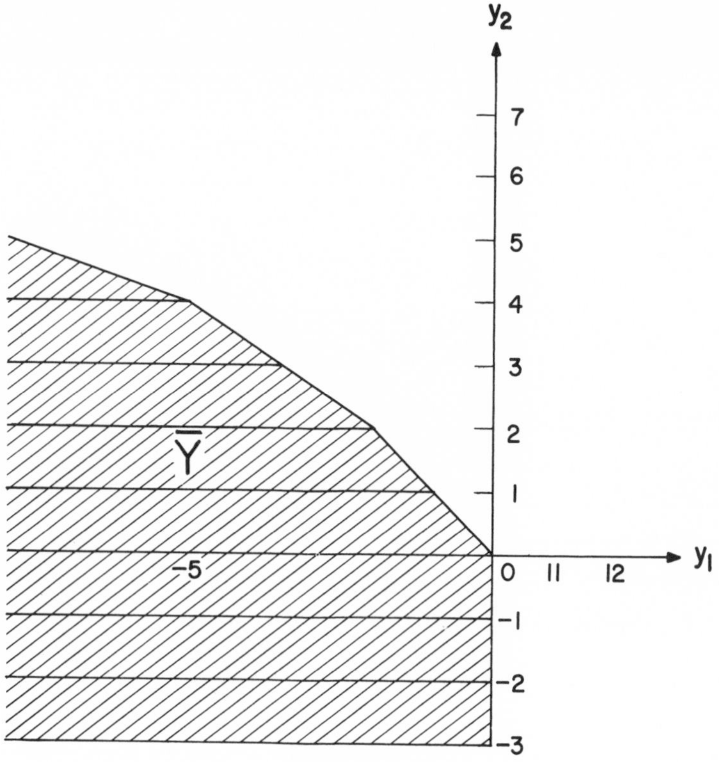


Figure 3.2

the vector $y$. For example, $[-\frac{5}{2}, \frac{17}{4}] = (-3, 4)$. If not all commodities are indivisible, then $[y]$ is understood to be a vector whose co-ordinates corresponding to indivisible commodities are the largest integers less than or equal to the corresponding elements of $y$, and all other elements of $[y]$ are the same as elements of $y$. Thus, for example, if $D$ consists of co-ordinates 1 and 3, then $[\frac{7}{5}, \frac{8}{9}, -\frac{21}{6}] = (1, \frac{8}{9}, -4)$. The following definitions will prove useful:

Definition 3.5.1. If $y$ belongs to $\bar{Y}$, the convex hull of $Y$, and if $y^* = y - [y]$, then $y_i^*$ is the excess capacity of the $i^{\text{th}}$ commodity if that commodity is an indivisible input or the completed part of the $i^{\text{th}}$ commodity if that commodity is an indivisible output.

Definition 3.5.2. The set $Y$ of production possibilities has the property of joint use of indivisible inputs and joint production of indivisible outputs if when $y^1$ belongs to $\bar{Y}$ and $y^2$ belongs to $\bar{Y}$, then $[y^1 + y^2]$ is a point in $Y$.

In many of the theorems to be proved later, the following postulate may be used instead of the postulate of integer convexity.

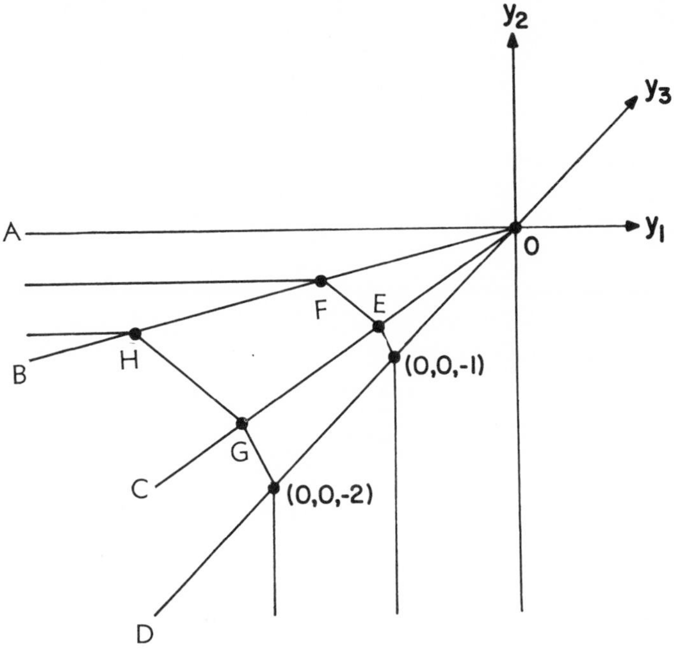


**Figure 3.3**

POSTULATE F (*joint use and joint production*). The set $Y$ of production possibilities has the property of joint use of indivisible inputs and the joint production of indivisible outputs.

Suppose $y^1$ and $y^2$ are contained in the convex hull $Y$. Now $y^* = y^1 - [y^1]$ and $y^{**} = y^2 - [y^2]$ are non-negative vectors. Thus $[y^1] = y^1 - y^*$ and $[y^2] = y^2 - y^{**}$ are points of $Y$ if the postulates of additivity and disposal are satisfied (Theorem 2.9.2). If the integer convexity postulate is satisfied then, since $[y^1]$ and $[y^2]$ are integer vectors, they are possible input-output combinations. If the $i^{\text{th}}$ commodity is indivisible and $y_i^1 \leqq 0$ and $y_i^2 \leqq 0$, then $y_i^*$ and $y_i^{**}$ may be viewed as excess capacities of the input $i$ associated with the possible points $[y^1]$ and $[y^2]$. By definition, the actual amount of the input $i$ used by these two processes, $[y_i^1]$ and $[y_i^2]$, is, of course, greater than or equal to (in absolute value) the amounts $y_i^1$ and $y_i^2$. If a unit of an indivisible input is used to less than capacity, the whole unit is counted as being occupied by the process $[y^1]$ or $[y^2]$. If the $i^{\text{th}}$ commodity is an indivisible output, $y_i^*$ and $y_i^{**}$ may be seen as the amounts of indivisible output $i$ which are completed only partially by the possible points $[y^1]$ and $[y^2]$.

If the postulate of joint use and joint production is satisfied, then the point $[y^1 + y^2]$ is a possible point. This possible point may be called the joint operation of the possible points $[y^1]$ and $[y^2]$. If $y_i^* + y_i^{**}$ is greater or equal to unity, then

$$[y_i^1 + y_i^2] > [y_i^1] + [y_i^2]$$

That is, if the $i^{\text{th}}$ commodity is an input, the joint production process $[y^1 + y^2]$ uses at least one unit less than the sum of amounts of that input used with the possible points $[y^1]$ and $[y^2]$. Hence, the term "joint use of indivisible inputs." If the total excess capacity of the $i^{\text{th}}$ input for the separate processes is greater than one unit of that input, the joint production process can get along with one less unit. If the $i^{\text{th}}$ commodity is an output, and the amounts of that output partially completed for the separate processes total to greater than one unit, the joint process produces one extra unit of that indivisible output.

Let us give a concrete example. Suppose there are five commodities: days of truck services, bricks at point A, bricks at point B, sand at point A, and sand at point B. Assume that one possible production process consists of hauling bricks from point A to point B and that the trip takes one whole day. This process may be represented by the possible input-output combination $(-1, -1, 1, 0, 0)$. This input-output combination indicates that one day of truck services as an input (the first co-ordinate) and one truckload of bricks at point A as an input (the second co-ordinate) may be used to produce one truckload of bricks at point B as an output (the third co-ordinate). Suppose there is another production process which consists of hauling sand from point A to point B which we represent by the input-output combination $(-1, 0, 0, -1, 1)$. One day of truck services and one truckload of sand at point A as inputs (the first and fourth co-ordinates, respectively) may be used to produce one truckload of sand at point B (the fifth co-ordinate).

Now if we wish to haul one-third of a truckload of bricks between point A and point B, the services of one truck for one day are still needed. It is impossible to use any fractional part of a day's truck services for hauling bricks from A to B because the trip takes one whole day. Thus days of truck services must be considered as an indivisible commodity for this purpose. Similarly, it is impossible to haul $\frac{2}{3}$ of a truckload of sand between points A and B by using less than one day of truck services. Thus the points

$$\begin{aligned} &(-1, -\tfrac{1}{3}, \tfrac{1}{3}, 0, 0) \\ &(-1, 0, 0, -\tfrac{2}{3}, \tfrac{2}{3}) \end{aligned} \tag{3.5.1}$$

are possible points while the points

$$\begin{aligned} (-1 + \tfrac{2}{3}, -\tfrac{1}{3}, \tfrac{1}{3}, 0, 0) &= (-\tfrac{1}{3}, -\tfrac{1}{3}, \tfrac{1}{3}, 0, 0) \\ (-1 + \tfrac{1}{3}, 0, 0, -\tfrac{2}{3}, \tfrac{2}{3}) &= (-\tfrac{2}{3}, 0, 0, -\tfrac{2}{3}, \tfrac{2}{3}) \end{aligned} \tag{3.5.2}$$

are not possible points. On the other hand, the points as given by (3.5.2) are convex combinations of the points $(-1, -1, 1, 0, 0)$ and $(0, 0, 0, 0, 0)$ and of the points $(-1, 0, 0, -1, 1)$ and $(0, 0, 0, 0, 0)$, respectively. Thus, given Postulate B (inaction) they belong to $\bar{Y}$, the convex hull of $Y$. Therefore, the points as given by (3.5.2) indicate that if anyone attempts to haul one-third of a truckload of bricks between A and B, two-thirds of the truck capacity will be unused.

Now if we haul the one-third of a truckload of bricks together with two-thirds of a truckload of sand only one day of truck services is needed. This combined operation may be represented by adding the two points as given by (3.5.2).

$$(-1 + \tfrac{2}{3}, -\tfrac{1}{3}, \tfrac{1}{3}, 0, 0) + (-1 + \tfrac{1}{3}, 0, 0, -\tfrac{2}{3}, \tfrac{2}{3}) = (-1, -\tfrac{1}{3}, \tfrac{1}{3}, \tfrac{2}{3}, \tfrac{2}{3})$$

That is, the combined process uses one less day of truck services than the sum of the number of days of truck services used by the two processes separately as indicated by the separate processes in (3.5.1). One day of truck services rather than two days of truck services are needed for the combined operation. This occurs because the excess capacities of the two separate operations (one-third and two-thirds of a truckload, respectively) add up to at least one whole day of truck services.

THEOREM 3.5.1. *Postulate A (additivity), B (inaction), C (disposal), D (closure), and E (integer convexity) imply Postulate F (joint use and joint production).*

*Proof:* Additivity implies that if $y^1 \in Y$ and $y^2 \in Y$, then $y^1 + y^2 \in Y$. If $y^* = y^1 + y^2 - [y^1 + y^2]$ then Theorem 2.9.2 implies that $[y^1 + y^2] = y^1 + y^2 - y^*$ belongs to $\bar{Y}$ since $y^*$ is non-negative. But since $[y^1 + y^2]$ is an integer vector, the integer convexity postulate implies that it belongs to $Y$. Thus Postulate F is satisfied.

THEOREM 3.5.2. *Postulates A (additivity), B (inaction), and F (joint use and joint production) imply Postulate E (integer convexity).*

*Proof:* Suppose $y$ is an integer vector and $y \in \bar{Y}$. Then additivity implies $y + 0 \in \bar{Y}$. Postulate F implies however, that $[y + 0] = y \in Y$. Thus the integer convexity postulate is satisfied.

This last theorem is particularly important in that it demonstrates that any theorem which assumes postulates A, B, and E is just as valid if one assumes postulate F (joint use and joint production) in place of postulate E (integer convexity). In many of the theorems discussed below we will assume postulates A, B, and E, but it is well to remember that these imply joint use and joint production.

## 3.6 Returns to Scale

Consider any point $y$. If we multiply $y$ by any non-negative scalar $\lambda$, we get a change in scale.

DEFINITION 3.6.1. If $0 \leqq \lambda \leqq 1$, then $\lambda \cdot y$ is a decrease in scale.

DEFINITION 3.6.2. If $\lambda > 1$, then $\lambda \cdot y$ is an increase in scale.

A decrease in scale is a proportionate decrease in all outputs concomitant with an equi-proportionate decrease (in absolute value terms) of all inputs. An increase in scale is a proportionate increase in all outputs with an equi-proportionate increase (in absolute value terms) of all inputs. Neither a decrease nor an increase in scale is necessarily possible.

Let us first consider the implications of integer convexity for the possibility of various changes in scale. If the set $Y$ satisfies postulates A (additivity), B (inaction), and E (integer convexity), then a non-integer change in scale $\lambda \cdot y$ is possible provided all $\lambda \cdot y_i$ are integer for all $i$ contained in $D$ (provided we change the scale of the input-output combination $y$ in a way which results in integer amounts for all indivisible commodities). Postulates A and B alone imply that all *integer* changes in scale are possible and the additional assumption of Postulate E implies the possibility of greater variations in scale. For example, suppose a set $Y$ of production possibilities contains the point $(6, -4)$. Postulates A and B imply that the point $(0, 0)$ and all positive integer multiples of the point $(6, -4)$, such as $(12, -8)$ and $(18, -12)$, are possible points. Now the convex hull $\bar{Y}$ of the set $Y$ contains some points $\lambda \cdot (6, -4)$ where $\lambda \geqq 0$ and where $\lambda$ is not necessarily integer. Thus, if in addition the set $Y$ is integer convex, then the points $\frac{1}{2}(6, -4) = (3, -2)$ and $\frac{3}{2}(6, -4) = (9, -6)$ are also possible input-output combinations.

Let us turn to a consideration of the *efficiency* of a decrease in scale.

THEOREM 3.6.1. *Given Postulates A (additivity), B (inaction), C (disposal), D (closure), and E (integer convexity), if $y$ is efficient and if $\lambda \cdot y$ is a possible decrease in scale, then $\lambda \cdot y$ is efficient.*

*Proof:* Suppose $\lambda \cdot y$ is not efficient. Then there is a point $y^*$ which belongs to $Y$ where $y^* \geq \lambda \cdot y$. The co-ordinates of $y^*$ may be written

$$y_i^* = \lambda \cdot y_i + \varepsilon_i \quad \text{for} \quad i = 1, \ldots, n$$

where $\varepsilon_i \geqq 0$ for all $i$ and $\varepsilon_i > 0$ for at least one $i$. Without loss of generality, we may assume that $\varepsilon_1 > 0$. If commodity 1 is indivisible, then $\varepsilon_1$ is an integer. Consider the point $(1/\lambda) \cdot y^*$. Since $1/\lambda \geqq 0$, by Lemma 2.6.1, the point $(1/\lambda) \cdot y^*$ belongs to $\bar{Y}$. Let

$$y^0 = (1/\lambda) \cdot y^* + \left(\frac{-\varepsilon_1(1 - \lambda)}{\lambda}, \frac{-\varepsilon_2}{\lambda}, \frac{-\varepsilon_3}{\lambda}, \ldots, \frac{-\varepsilon_n}{\lambda}\right)$$

$$= (y_1 + \varepsilon_1, y_2, y_3, \ldots, y_n).$$

Since $-\varepsilon_i \leqq 0$ for $i = 1, \ldots, n$ and since $(1 - \lambda) \geqq 0$, $y^0$ is the sum of a point $(1/\lambda) \cdot y^*$ belonging to $\bar{Y}$ and a non-positive vector. According to Theorem 2.9.2, $y^0$ belongs to $\bar{Y}$. Now $y^0 \geq y$ since $\varepsilon_1 > 0$. Since $\varepsilon_1$ is integer if commodity 1 is indivisible, and since $y^0$ belongs to $\bar{Y}$, integer convexity implies that $y^0$ belongs to $Y$ as well. Thus $y$ is not efficient, which is a contradition.

Therefore, if an efficient point is decreased in scale and the decrease in scale is possible, then such a decrease in scale is always efficient. Now suppose $y$ is an efficient input-output combination. If we increase the scale of the efficient point $y$ and obtain a possible point, we are not certain that this increase in scale is efficient. We shall construct an example of a set $Y$ of production possibilities which satisfies Postulate A (additivity), B (inaction), C (disposal), and E (integer convexity) and which contains an efficient point which is not efficient for a possible increase in scale.

Consider a set $Y$ which has a convex hull consisting of all points $y$ which satisfy the following equations and inequalities:

$$y_1 = -3x_1 \qquad y_2 = 2x_1 - x_2 \tag{3.6.1}$$

where

$$x_1 \geqq 0, \qquad x_2 \geqq 0. \tag{3.6.2}$$

Suppose the set $Y$ satisfies Postulate E. Then the set $Y$ consists of all points $y$ which satisfy (3.6.1) and (3.6.2) and also the restriction

$$y_1 \text{ is integer} \qquad y_2 \text{ is integer.} \tag{3.6.3}$$

We shall demonstrate that the set $Y$ as determined by (3.6.1), (3.6.2), and (3.6.3) satisfies Postulates A, B, and C.

If $(y_1', y_2') = (-3x_1', 2x_1' - x_2')$ and $(y_1'', y_2'') = (-3x_1'', 2x_1'' - x_2'')$ are points of $Y$, then the sum $(y_1', y_2') + (y_1'', y_2'')$ may be written

$$y_1' + y_1'' = -3(x_1' + x_1'')$$
$$y_2' + y_2'' = 2(x_1' + x_1'') - (x_2' + x_2'')$$

Thus equation (3.6.1) is satisfied, and it is obvious that (3.6.2) is also satisfied. If $y_1'$ and $y_1''$ are both integer, certainly their sum is integer, and if $y_2'$ and $y_2''$ are integer then their sum is integer. Thus (3.6.3) is satisfied. Therefore Postulate A must hold.

If $x_1 = 0$ and $x_2 = 0$, then from (3.6.1) we see that $y_1 = 0$ and $y_2 = 0$. Thus Postulate B is satisfied.

If $x_1 = 0$ and $x_2 = 1$, from (3.6.1) we get $y_1 = 0$ and $y_2 = -1$. If $x_1 = \frac{1}{3}$ and $x_2 = \frac{2}{3}$, from (3.6.1) we get $y_1 = -1$ and $y_2 = 0$. That is, we may dispose either one unit of commodity 1 or one unit of commodity 2, and Postulate C is satisfied.

The set $Y$ is pictured in Figure 3.4. The shaded area is $\bar{Y}$, the convex hull of $Y$, and the set $Y$ itself consists of all the heavy dots (lattice points) within the shaded area. The point $(-2, 1)$ is efficient[2] and represents an input of two units of commodity 1 and an output of one unit of commodity 2. The points $\lambda \cdot (-2, 1)$ for any non-negative integer $\lambda$ are not efficient, however. For example, if $\lambda = 2$, then the point $(-4, 2)$ is not efficient since the point $(-3, 2)$ is possible and uses fewer inputs of commodity 1 to produce the same amount of output of commodity 2.

On the other hand, the point $(-3, 2)$ is efficient[3] and any integer multiple of this point is efficient. For example, the points $(-6, 4)$ and $(-9, 6)$ are efficient.

The above discussion leads to a partitioning of the possible points into two classes, those for which all possible increases in scale are efficient and those for which all possible increases in scale are not necessarily efficient.

DEFINITION 3.6.3. A possible point $y$ exhibits constant returns for possible increases in scale if every possible increase in scale is efficient.

DEFINITION 3.6.4. A possible point exhibits increasing returns for possible increases in scale if at least one possible increase in scale is not efficient.

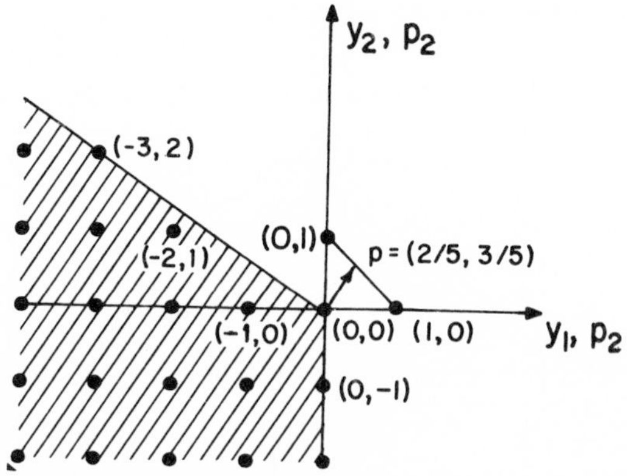


Figure 3.4

[2] *Proof:* The point $(-2, 1)$ is not efficient if there exists a possible point $(-2 + k_1, 1 + k_2)$ where $k_1$ and $k_2$ are non-negative integers and where either $k_1$ or $k_2$ are positive. If we substitute $y_1 = -2 + k_1$ and $y_2 = 1 + k_2$ into (3.6.1), we obtain upon solving for $x_1$ and $x_2$:

$$x_1 = \tfrac{2}{3} - \tfrac{1}{3}k_1$$
$$x_2 = \tfrac{1}{3} - \tfrac{2}{3}k_1 - k_2.$$

If either $k_1$ or $k_2$ is a positive integer, $x_2$ must be negative. Since $x_2$ is constrained to be non-negative, the point $(-2, 1)$ must be efficient.

[3] The proof may be demonstrated in the same manner as in the previous footnote.

In Figure 3.4, the point $(-2, 1)$ exhibits increasing returns while the point $(-3, 2)$ exhibits constant returns for possible increases in scale. In general terms, if it is not possible with less than a doubling, tripling, etc. of all inputs (in absolute value terms) to obtain a similar multiplication of all outputs, then a possible point exhibits constant returns. If any output may be more than doubled with a doubling of all other inputs and outputs or if any input may be less than doubled (in absolute value terms) with a doubling of all other inputs and outputs. then an input-output combination exhibits increasing returns for integer changes in scale.

In order to see more clearly the relationship between indivisible commodities, integer convexity, and increasing returns, we shall introduce an additional concept, that of efficiency with respect to $\bar{Y}$. The concept of efficiency which we introduced in Chapter 2 is very similar to that of efficiency with respect to $\bar{Y}$, but the two concepts are not equivalent. A possible point $y$ may be efficient but not efficient with respect to $\bar{Y}$.

Definition 3.6.5. A point $y^*$ belonging to $Y$ is efficient with respect to $\bar{Y}$ if and only if there exists no other point $y^{**}$ belonging to $\bar{Y}$ such that $y^{**} \geq y^*$, i.e., $y_i^{**} \geqq y_i^*$ for all $i$ and $y_i^{**} > y_i^*$ for at least one $i$.

Geometrically, if a point $y^*$ is efficient with respect to $\bar{Y}$, then there exist no points of $\bar{Y}$ above and to the right of $y^*$. If there are no points of $Y$ above and to the right of the possible point $y^*$ but there are points of $\bar{Y}$ above and to the right of $y^*$, then $y^*$ is efficient, but $y^*$ is not efficient with respect to $\bar{Y}$. To illustrate these ideas graphically, we may turn back to Figure 3.4. The point $(-3, 2)$ is both efficient and efficient with respect to $\bar{Y}$ since there are no points of $Y$ and no points of $\bar{Y}$ which lie above and to the right of the point $(-3, 2)$. On the other hand the point $(-2, 1)$ is efficient but is not efficient with respect to $\bar{Y}$. There are no points of $Y$ above and to the right of the point $(-2, 1)$ but there are points of $\bar{Y}$ above and to the right of $(-2, 1)$. Finally, the point $(-1, 0)$ is neither efficient nor efficient with respect to $\bar{Y}$.

To say that a point $y^*$ exhibits increasing returns for integer changes in scale is equivalent to saying that $y^*$ is not efficient with respect to $\bar{Y}$. That is, we may prove the following theorem:

Theorem 3.6.2. *Given Postulates $A$ (additivity), $B$ (inaction), $C$ (disposal), $D$ (closure), and $E$ (integer convexity), a possible point $y^*$ exhibits increasing returns for integer changes in scale if and only if $y^*$ is not efficient with respect to $\bar{Y}$.*

*Proof:* Suppose $y^*$ exhibits increasing returns for integer changes in scale. We shall demonstrate that $y^*$ is thus not efficient with respect to $\bar{Y}$. If $y^*$ exhibits increasing returns for integer changes in scale, then for some positive integer $\lambda$ the point $\lambda \cdot y^*$ is not efficient. Thus there exists a possible point $y^{**}$ where $y_i^{**} \geqq \lambda \cdot y_i^*$ for all $i$ and $y_i^{**} > \lambda \cdot y_i^*$ for at least one $i$. In other words,

$$y_i^{**} = \lambda \cdot y_i^* + \varepsilon_i \quad \text{for} \quad i = 1, \ldots, n$$

where $\varepsilon_i \geqq 0$ for all $i$ and $\varepsilon_i > 0$ for at least one $i$. Consider the point $(1/\lambda) \cdot y^{**}$. Since $\lambda$ is a positive integer, we have $1/\lambda \leqq 1$. Since $\bar{Y}$ is a convex cone with vertex the origin (Theorem 2.9.1), $(1/\lambda) \cdot y^{**} \in \bar{Y}$. Now it is clearly evident that

$$(1/\lambda) \cdot y_i^{**} = y_i^* + \varepsilon_i/\lambda \geqq y_i^* \quad \text{for} \quad i = 1, \ldots, n.$$

Since $\varepsilon_i > 0$ for at least one $i$, we see that $(1/\lambda) \cdot y_i^{**} > y_i^*$ for at least one $i$. Therefore $y^*$ is not efficient with respect to $\bar{Y}$.

Now suppose $y^*$ is not efficient with respect to $\bar{Y}$. We wish to show that $y^*$ exhibits increasing returns. Since $y^*$ is not efficient with respect to $\bar{Y}$, there exists a point $y^{**}$ where $y^{**} \in \bar{Y}$ and $y_i^{**} \geqq y_i^*$ for all $i$ with $y_i^{**} > y_i^*$ for at least one $i$. We have, therefore,

$$y_i^{**} = y_i^* + \varepsilon_i \quad \text{for} \quad i = 1, \ldots, n$$

where $\varepsilon_i \geqq 0$ for all $i$ and $\varepsilon_i > 0$ for at least one $i$. Without loss of generality we may assume that $\varepsilon_1 > 0$. Then let $\lambda'$ be a positive scalar which solves the equation

$$\lambda' \cdot \varepsilon_1 = 1 \tag{3.6.4}$$

Let $[\lambda']$ be the largest integer which is less than or equal to $\lambda'$. Then

$$\lambda' = [\lambda'] + f \tag{3.6.5}$$

where $f$ is a non-negative fraction. Let $\lambda$ be a positive integer which satisfies the equation

$$\lambda = [\lambda'] + 1. \tag{3.6.6}$$

From (3.6.5) and (3.6.6) we see that

$$\lambda = \lambda' + 1 - f. \tag{3.6.7}$$

According to Theorem 2.9.1, $\lambda \cdot y^{**}$ belongs to $\bar{Y}$ since $\lambda$ is a positive scalar. According to Theorem 2.9.2, we may add the non-positive vector

$$(-\varepsilon_1(1 - f), -\lambda\varepsilon_2, -\lambda \cdot \varepsilon_3, \ldots, -\lambda \cdot \varepsilon_n)$$

to $\lambda \cdot y^{**}$ to obtain another point of $\bar{Y}$. Using (3.6.4) and (3.6.7) we obtain the result

$$y^0 = (\lambda \cdot y_1^* + 1, \lambda \cdot y_2^*, \lambda y_3^*, \ldots, \lambda \cdot y_n^*)$$

which is also a point of $Y$ since $\lambda$ is a positive integer (Postulate E). Now from Postulate A, $\lambda \cdot y^*$ belongs to $Y$, but $\lambda \cdot y^*$ is not efficient since $y^0 \geq \lambda \cdot y^*$.

## 3.7 Profit Maximization and Increasing Returns

Theorem 2.12.1 (efficiency) shows that every profit-maximizing possible point is efficient with a positive price vector $p > 0$. We suggested that the converse is not necessarily true; that there is not necessarily some positive price vector which makes any particular efficient point a profit-maximizing possible point. In fact, the following theorem shows that if any efficient point exhibits increasing returns for integer changes in scale, it is impossible to find a competitive price system such that the efficient point is a profit-maximizing possible point.

THEOREM 3.7.1. *Given Postulates A (additivity) and B (inaction), if an efficient point $y^*$ exhibits increasing returns for integer changes in scale, then there exists no competitive price system, $p(y) = p > 0$ for all $y \in Y$, such that $y^*$ is a profit-maximizing possible point.*

*Proof:* Suppose there does exist a competitive price system, $p(y) = p$, such that $y^*$ is a profit-maximizing possible point. According to Theorem 2.11.2, $p \cdot y^* = 0$. Furthermore, if $\lambda$ is any positive integer, $\lambda \cdot y^* \in Y$ because of Postulate A. Since $p \cdot (\lambda \cdot y^*) = 0$, the point $\lambda \cdot y^*$ is a profit-maximizing possible point. According to Theorem 2.12.1, the point $y^*$ is efficient. Since, however, the point $y^*$ exhibits increasing returns, for some positive integer $\lambda$ the point $\lambda \cdot y^*$ is not efficient, which is a contradiction.

We also have the following corollary:

COROLLARY 3.7.1. *Given the competitive price system, $p(y) = p > 0$ for all $y \in Y$, if there exists a profit-maximizing possible point, and if $y^*$ exhibits increasing returns for integer changes in scale, then $p \cdot y^* < 0$.*

*Proof:* Suppose $y^{**}$ is a profit-maximizing possible point. If $p \cdot y^* > 0$, then $y^{**}$ could not be profit-maximizing according to Theorem 2.11.2. If $p \cdot y^* = 0$, then since $p \cdot y^{**} = 0$ (Theorem 2.11.2), the point $y^*$ must be a profit-maximizing possible point. This contradicts Theorem 3.7.1. Thus, $p \cdot y^* < 0$.

Therefore, if a profit-maximizing possible point exists, any efficient input-output combination which exhibits increasing returns to scale *can only be operated at a loss.*

*Theorem* 3.7.1 and its corollary may be illustrated with the use of the set $Y$ which is pictured in Figure 3.4 above. In this graphical representation, the set $Y$ of production possibilities is described by equations (3.6.1), (3.6.2), and (3.6.3). The set $Y$ consists of all the heavy dots within the shaded area. The convex hull of $Y$ is the shaded area. Consider the point $(-2, 1)$ which exhibits increasing returns for integer changes in scale. This point is not efficient with respect to $\bar{Y}$, the convex hull of $Y$. Also, note that the point $(-2, 1)$ does not lie in the boundary of $\bar{Y}$. We shall demonstrate the assertion that for any conceivable competitive price system, the point $(-2, 1)$ is not profit-maximizing. The set of all conceivable competitive price systems may be represented by the prices $p_1 = \frac{2}{5} + v$ and $p_2 = \frac{3}{5} - v$, which are the respective prices on commodities 1 and 2 where $v$ may take on any value such that $p_1 > 0$ and $p_2 > 0$. The prices $p_1$ and $p_2$ represent a normalized set where $p_1 + p_2 = 1$. Now if $v < 0$, the profit of the possible point $(-3, 2)$ is $(p_1, p_2) \cdot (-3, 2) = (\frac{2}{5} + v, \frac{3}{5} - v) \cdot (-3, 2) = -3v - 2v > 0$. The profit of the point $(-3, 2)$ is positive and according to Theorem 2.11.2, no profit-maximizing possible point exists. On the other hand, if $v \geqq 0$, the profit of the point $(-2, 1)$ is $(\frac{2}{5} + v, \frac{3}{5} - v) \cdot (-2, 1) = -\frac{1}{5} - 3v < 0$. The profit of the point $(-2, 1)$ is negative and according to Theorem 2.11.2, the point $(-2, 1)$ cannot be a profit-maximizing possible point. In the one case $(v < 0)$, we demonstrated that no profit-maximizing possible point exists, and in the other case $(v \geqq 0)$, we showed that $(-2, 1)$ could not possibly be profit-maximizing. In either case the point $(-2, 1)$, which exhibits increasing returns, is not a profit-maximizing possible point. If $v = 0$, however, one can show that a profit-maximizing possible point exists and the profits of the point $(-2, 1)$ are negative. In this case, the point $(-2, 1)$, which exhibits increasing returns, can only be operated at a loss.

## 3.8 Conclusions

This chapter introduced the notion of an indivisible commodity into the analysis of production. Some authors maintain that examples of indivisible commodities are extremely rare or even perhaps non-existent. Such arguments are usually attempts to justify an assumption of complete divisibility of all commodities by claiming that one can in fact divide seemingly indivisible commodities by choosing a proper measure for such commodities. For example, Chamberlin writes, "It would appear that one meaningful and realistic way to divide a unit of labor is on a time basis."[4] Stigler maintains that in the case of the commodity trucks, "If one wishes one-fifth of a truck for a week, he can hire a truck for a day, and in general the time dimension offers wide opportunities for achieving divisibility of production services."[5]

This approach, however, ignores the problem of definition. We must either define the labor factor in such a way that we measure its amount in terms of the number of men, or we must define it in terms of hours of labor service. The factor, trucks, is measured in terms of number of trucks or days of truck service, not both. In the one case the factor is a

[4] E. H. Chamberlin, *The Theory of Monopolistic Competition* (7th edn. Cambridge: Harvard University Press, 1956), p. 240.

[5] G. Stigler, *The Theory of Price* (New York: Macmillan, 1952), p. 137.

good; in the other case it is a service. In fact, for some considerations we may want to define trucks both as a good and as a service and specify that these are two separate commodities. For example, consider the case of a truck rental firm and suppose that commodities are dated. Trucks at time $t = 0$ can be considered as an input and truck services at times $t \geqq 0$ as outputs for a possible production activity of the truck rental firm. The distinction between the two commodities may be useful in the analysis of such a firm, and the failure to make the distinction would be an example of "defining away the problem."

Other authors argue that "in addition to the time basis just discussed, another meaningful and realistic way to achieve continuous divisibility of a factor is to change it qualitatively."[6] This alternative is objectionable on the same grounds as that of using the time dimension as a basis for attaining divisibility. Commodities of different quality may be considered different commodities, and such a distinction may be desirable for some purposes. Stigler carries this notion of quality difference very far indeed when he suggests that in order to achieve divisibility, "From a broader point of view one may use trucks instead of railroads, ferries or detours instead of bridges, et cetera."[7] While there may be instances where land transportation services may be considered as one factor and water crossing devices as another factor, there will certainly be some problems where there is a need to make a finer distinction. Even where quality differences occur in a continuous fashion, it may be necessary to choose a certain finite number of quality levels and define a commodity for each of these levels. A commodity of any level of quality would be put in one of the finite classes of commodities.

Finally, it has been argued that divisibility may be achieved by a money measure of various factors of production. A case in point is Mrs. Joan Robinson's attempt to derive a demand curve for a factor by speaking of the "marginal product per unit of outlay."[8] Machlup offers a very cogent criticism of this device: "By measuring units of a factor in terms of their market value, marginal productivity analysis is, to my mind, reduced *ad absurdum*. One must bear in mind that marginal productivity analysis as part of the theory of distribution is to serve as an explanation of the market values of factors or services. To define their services in terms of these market values is to give up the task of explaining them."[9]

None of these attempts to assume away the problem of indivisibility is very convincing. In many concrete situations the effects of indivisibilities

[6] Chamberlin, *The Theory of Monopolistic Competition*, p. 241.

[7] G. Stigler, *The Theory of Price*, p. 138.

[8] J. V. Robinson, "Euler's Theorem and the Problem of Distribution," *Economic Journal*, Vol. 44 (Sept. 1934), p. 412.

[9] F. Machlup, "On the Meaning of Marginal Product," *Explorations in Economics: Notes and Essays Contributed in Honor of F. W. Taussig* (New York: McGraw Hill, 1936), p. 255.

cannot be ignored or defined away. They can and do affect the answers to a whole range of decision problems and policy questions.

The consequences of introducing indivisible commodities into a theory of production are that it allows for the consideration of a certain type of increasing returns to scale, about which there has been much controversy. Kaldor[10] and others[11] have maintained that increasing returns are solely a result of indivisibilities. Chamberlin,[12] on the other hand, insists that increasing returns to scale can only be a result of changing quality of factors and specialization of factors. Specialization of factors, however, is only an efficient way of production if each unit of a factor can give its undivided attention to the performance of certain specific tasks. Some highly specialized factors such as complicated, large, expensive machinery are only useful at performing very specific tasks, and these machines often must be a certain critical minimum size. Other specialized factors, such as labor, may be able to perform a variety of tasks, but if they are switched from task to task very frequently there is a loss in time in moving from task to task. In other words, the services of these factors are not perfectly divisible; and once they are committed to a certain job, there is a required minimum effort. It seems that the phenomenon of specialization is inextricably wound up with the fact that certain factors are not perfectly divisible. In fact, Koopmans flatly stated that he has "not found one example of increasing returns to scale in which there is not some indivisible commodity in the surrounding circumstances."[13] In any case it seems to be begging the question to argue whether increasing returns are caused by indivisibilities, specialization, or anything else.[14] One should rather ask which explanation is the most useful or illuminating for a specific purpose.

One must be careful to distinguish between increasing returns to scale because of fixed factors and increasing returns due to indivisibilities which may occur even without fixed factors. The former type of increasing returns is usually discussed in terms of the "spreading of overhead" which causes average costs to fall over some initial range of output.[15]

[10] N. Kaldor, "The Equilibrium of the Firm," *Economic Journal*, Vol. 44 (March 1934), p. 36.

[11] F. H. Hahn, "Proportionality, Divisibility and Economies of Scales: [one of] Two Comments," *Quarterly Journal of Economics*, Vol. 63 (Feb. 1949), p. 131; A. N. McLeod, "Proportionality, Divisibility and Economics of Scale: [one of] Two Comments," *Quarterly Journal of Economics*, Vol. 63 (Feb. 1949), p. 128; and Joseph Lerner, "Constant Proportions, Fixed Plant and Optimum Conditions of Production," *Quarterly Journal of Economics*, Vol. 16 (Aug. 1949), p. 215.

[12] E. H. Chamberlin, *The Theory of Monopolistic Competition*, Appendix B, pp. 230–259.

[13] T. C. Koopmans, *Three Essays on the State of Economic Science* (New York: McGraw Hill, 1957). p. 152n.

[14] T. M. Whitin and M. H. Peston in "Random Variations, Risk and Returns to Scale," *Quarterly Journal of Economics*, Vol. 68 (Nov. 1954), pp. 603–612, argue that increasing returns are caused by probability considerations.

[15] See Jacob Viner, "Cost Curves and Supply Curves," in G. Stigler and K. Boulding, eds., *Readings in Price Theory* (Homewood, Illinois: Irwin, 1952), pp. 202–203, 213.

A "spreading of overhead" occurs only when there are certain fixed factors which are not freely variable and which give rise to unavoidable fixed costs. Because these costs are fixed and incurred regardless of output, they ought to play no part in the calculations of a profit-maximizing entrepreneur. In our model of production we postulate the possibility of inaction, that is, the entrepreneur has the choice of employing no inputs if he desires to produce no outputs. We assume factors are freely variable and that no fixed expenses need be incurred. This does not preclude the possibility that the cost of an indivisible input remains invariant over certain ranges of output. Once the choice is made to produce any output at all, the cost of a whole unit of an indivisible input may be incurred although that unit may not be used to capacity. The entrepreneur still has the choice, however, of avoiding this expense by producing no output at all.[16]

Finally, another implication of indivisible commodities is that in situations where there are increasing returns, a perfectly competitive pricing system results in negative profits or losses. To quote from Abba Lerner, "with significant indivisibility, perfect competition must result in the firm's running at a loss."[17] Increasing returns situations are not amenable to the usual sort of profit-maximization analysis with competitive pricing arrangements.

[16] For a discussion of this distinction see W. Arthur Lewis, "Fixed Costs," *Economica*, Vol. 13 [new series] (Nov. 1946), p. 235.

[17] Abba P. Lerner, *The Economics of Control* (New York: Macmillan, 1944), p. 177.

# CHAPTER 4

## *SUBSTITUTION AND PRICE DISCRIMINATION*

### 4.1 Introduction

"The concept of substitutability is one of the most important in the whole of economic analysis."[1] Usually, substitution refers to the fact that a production isoquant is convex, but we define and discuss substitution not in terms of isoquants but in terms of the set $Y$ of production possibilities. We consider two different types of substitution, direct and indirect. Roughly, indirect substitution refers to instances where an input-output combination must be increased in scale before substitution can take place. These concepts are crucial to our discussion in Chapter 5.

In this chapter, we also discuss the notion of discriminatory pricing. Given a price-quantity relationship, discrimination means that, because each unit may be sold at a different price, the revenue (or cost) accruing to a given amount of a commodity is an integral rather than a simple price times quantity expression. Profit is a sum of revenues and costs, that is, profit is a sum of integrals, not a vector product.

### 4.2 Substitution

In the traditional theory of production, substitution generally implies that for a given output of one commodity (or a given set of outputs for several commodities in the case of joint production), different factor proportions are possible. Substitution also takes place between outputs. For example, the notion of substitutability is implicit in the use of product transformation curves. If the marginal rate of transformation is defined, it implies that one output (e.g. guns) may be substituted for another (e.g. butter) with a given set of resources as inputs.

First, let us define direct or strong substitution.

DEFINITION 4.2.1. Given a point $y$ in $Y$, the $j^{\text{th}}$ commodity is a *direct substitute* for the $k^{\text{th}}$ commodity if and only if there exists a $y^*$ in $Y$ such that

$$y_k^* > y_k, \qquad y_i^* \geqq y_i \quad \text{for} \quad i \neq j \quad \text{and} \quad i \neq k, \quad \text{and} \quad y_j^* < y_j$$

Substitution is defined with respect to a particular input-output combination. That is, given the input-output combination $y'$, commodity $j$ may be a direct substitute for commodity $k$. On the other hand, given the input-output combination $y''$ it is not necessarily true that commodity $j$ is a substitute for commodity $k$.

[1] K. E. Boulding, *Economic Analysis* (New York: Harper, 1941), p. 489.

To further elaborate on Definition 4.2.1, we may consider four possible cases: (*a*) commodities $j$ and $k$ are both inputs, (*b*) commodities $j$ and $k$ are both outputs, (*c*) commodity $j$ is an input and commodity $k$ is an output, and (*d*) commodity $j$ is an output and commodity $k$ is an input. In each of the four respective cases, for a given input-output combination $y$, if commodity $j$ is a direct substitute for commodity $k$, then

(*a*) more of input $j$ (in absolute value terms) and less of input $k$ (in absolute value terms) may be used along with no more (in absolute value) of all other inputs to produce no less than the original amounts of all outputs;
(*b*) less of output $j$ and more of output $k$ along with no less of any other output may be produced by using no more than the original amounts of all inputs;
(*c*) more of input $j$ along with no more of all other inputs may be used to produce more of output $k$ and no less of all other outputs; or
(*d*) less of output $j$ and no less of all other outputs may be produced with less of input $k$ and no more of all other inputs.

If the $j^{th}$ commodity is a direct substitute for commodity $k$, this in no way implies that the $k^{th}$ commodity is a direct substitute for the $j^{th}$ commodity. As an illustration, let us consider Figure 4.1. This is a projection

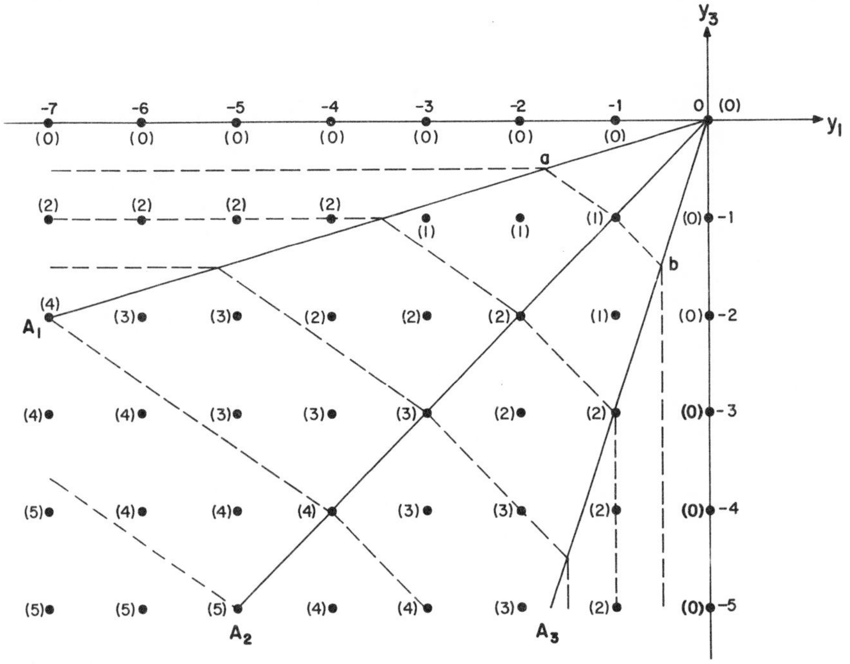


Figure 4.1

of a set $Y$ of production possibilities in three dimensions onto the two-dimensional subspace of commodities 1 and 3. All points with integer co-ordinates in the non-positive (lower left) quadrant in this figure are projections of possible points. Any points which are indicated by the number 2 in parentheses represent the various amounts of commodities 1 and 3 which may be used as inputs to produce a given amount (2 units) of commodity 2 as an output. Consider the point $(y_1, y_3) = (-1, -3)$ in Figure 4.1 where $y_2$ is equal to the number in parentheses, i.e., $y_2 = 2$. Then for the point $y = (y_1, y_2, y_3) = (-1, 2, -3)$, commodity 1 is a direct substitute for commodity 3 because the point $y^* = (y_1^*, y_2^*, y_3^*)$ where $(y_1^*, y_3^*) = (-2, -2)$ and $y_2^* = 2$ is such that $y_1^* = -2 < y_1 = -1$, $y_2^* = 2 \geqq y_2 = 2$, and $y_3^* = -2 > y_3 = -3$. That is, more of commodity 1 (in absolute value terms) and less of commodity 3 (in absolute value terms) may be used as inputs to produce at least 2 units of commodity 2 as an output. On the other hand, commodity 3 is not a direct substitute for commodity 1 since the only other possible points which use more of input 3 to produce 2 units or more of output 2, use no less of input 1.

Consider the point $(y_1, y_3) = (-2, -2)$ in Figure 4.1 where $y_2 = 2$ (the figure in parentheses), i.e., the point $(y_1, y_2, y_3) = (-2, 2, -2)$. Commodity 3 is a substitute for commodity 1 since there exists a possible point $(y_1^*, y_2^*, y_3^*) = (-1, 2, -3)$ which uses less (in absolute value terms) of commodity 1 and more (in absolute value terms) of commodity 3 as inputs to produce no less than 2 units of commodity 2. We also see that commodity 1 is a substitute for commodity 3 since the possible point $(y_1^{**}, y_2^{**}, y_3^{**}) = (-4, 2, -1)$ uses more of input 1 and less of input 2 to produce no less than 2 units of output 2. Thus, with the efficient point $(-2, 2, -2)$, substitutability runs in both directions as regards commodities 1 and 3.

A somewhat weaker notion of substitutability is that of indirect substitutability.

DEFINITION 4.2.2. Given a point $y$ in $Y$, the $j^{\text{th}}$ commodity is an indirect substitute for the $k^{\text{th}}$ commodity if and only if there exists a $y^*$ in $Y$ such that for some positive integer $\lambda$, $y_k^* > \lambda \cdot y_k$, $y_i^* \geqq \lambda \cdot y_i$ for $i \neq j, k$, and $y_j^* < \lambda \cdot y_j$.

Suppose the $j^{\text{th}}$ and $k^{\text{th}}$ commodities are inputs and all other commodities are outputs for the efficient input-output combination $y$. Then the $j^{\text{th}}$ commodity is an indirect or weak substitute for the $k^{\text{th}}$ commodity provided that *for some integer change in scale* a possible input-output combination exists which uses less (in absolute value terms) of the $k^{\text{th}}$ commodity and more (in absolute value terms) of the $j^{\text{th}}$ commodity as inputs to produce no less than the scaled-up amounts of all outputs.

Direct substitution, implies indirect substitution, *but not conversely.*

That is, if the $j^{\text{th}}$ commodity is a direct substitute for the $k^{\text{th}}$ commodity, then the $j^{\text{th}}$ commodity is an indirect substitute for the $k^{\text{th}}$ commodity where the integer $\lambda = 1$. On the other hand, if the $j^{\text{th}}$ commodity is an indirect substitute for the $k^{\text{th}}$ commodity, then it is not necessarily true that the $j^{\text{th}}$ commodity is a direct substitute for the $k^{\text{th}}$ commodity.

Given a possible point $y$, if the $j^{\text{th}}$ commodity is an indirect substitute for the $k^{\text{th}}$ commodity then for some positive integer $\lambda$, there exists a point $y^*$ in $Y$ such that $y_k^* > \lambda \cdot y_k$, $y_i^* \geqq \lambda \cdot y_i$ for $i \neq j, k$, and $y_j^* < \lambda \cdot y_j$. If we divide these inequalities on both sides by $\lambda$, then we get $(1/\lambda) \cdot y_k^* > y_k$, $(1/\lambda) \cdot y_i^* > y_i$ for $i \neq j$, $k$, and $(1/\lambda) \cdot y_j^* < y_j$. Now if Postulate B (inaction) is satisfied, the point $(1/\lambda) \cdot y^* \in \bar{Y}$, the convex hull of $Y$ because $0 < (1/\lambda) \leqq 1$ and $(1/\lambda) \cdot y^*$ is a convex combination of 0 and $y^*$ which both belong to $Y$. Hence, given Postulate B, indirect substitutability implies that there exists a $y^{**} = (1/\lambda) \cdot y^* \in \bar{Y}$ such that $y_k^{**} > y_k$, $y_i^{**} \geqq y_i$ for $i \neq j$, $k$, and $y_j^{**} < y_j$. One might say that given Postulate B, indirect substitutability with respect to $Y$ implies direct substitutability with respect to $\bar{Y}$.

To illustrate these concepts let us consider the set $Y$ which is pictured in Figures 4.1 and 4.2. The convex hull of $Y$ is the convex cone spanned by the three rays $A_1$, $A_2$, $A_3$ and the non-positive parts of the $y_1$, $y_2$, and $y_3$ axes in Figure 4.2. The set $Y$ consists of all integer points within this convex cone. The set $Y$ satisfies all four postulates; A (additivity), B (inaction), C (disposal), and D (integer convexity). Figure 4.1 is a projection onto the two-dimensional subspace of commodities 1 and 3. All integer points in the non-negative (lower left) quadrant are projections of possible points. The figures in parentheses indicate maximum amounts of commodity 2 which are possible for various combinations of commodities 1 and 3 as inputs.

Consider the point $(-1, -1)$ in Figure 4.1. The output of commodity 2 associated with this point is 1 unit. There are no possible points which use less of input 1 and more of input 3 while giving no less than one unit of output 2. Nor are there any possible points which use more of input 1 and less of input 3 while giving no less than one unit of output 2. Thus commodity 1 is not a *direct* substitute for commodity 3 and commodity 3 is not a *direct* substitute for commodity 1. On the other hand, let us increase the scale of the point $(-1, -1)$ by 3 times (a positive integer amount) to $(-3, -3)$. The maximum possible amount of commodity 2 is then 3 units. For the point $(-7, -2)$ the maximum possible amount of commodity 2 is 4 units. Hence it is possible to increase the scale of $(-1, -1)$ by three to $(-3, -3)$ and find a possible point $(-7, -2)$ which uses more of input 1 and less of input 3 while resulting in no fewer than 3 units (in this case more than 3 units) of commodity 2 as an output. Thus commodity 3 is an indirect substitute for commodity 1. Next let us increase the scale of $(-1, -1)$ by two to $(-2, -2)$. The

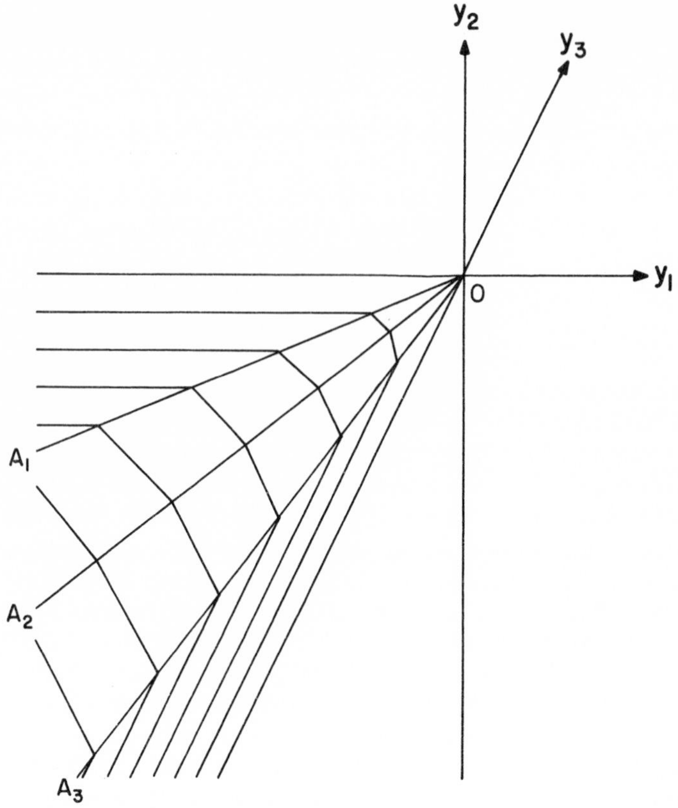


Figure 4.2

maximum possible output of commodity 2 is two units. The maximum possible output of commodity 2 for the point $(-1, -3)$ is likewise two units. It is possible to increase the scale of $(-1, -1)$ by two to $(-2, -2)$ and find a possible point $(-1, -3)$ which uses less of input 1 and more of input 3 while resulting in no fewer than 2 units of output 2. Hence commodity 1 is an *indirect* substitute for commodity 3.

The dashed broken line segments in Figure 4.1 represent projections of points in the boundary of the convex hull $\bar{Y}$ of $Y$. We shall call these dashed broken line segments iso-metric lines (to distinguish them from isoquants). Any point on the iso-metric line which passes through $(-1, -1)$ represents a point $y$ in the boundary of $\bar{Y}$ where $y_2 = 1$. Any point on the iso-metric line through $(-2, -2)$ represents a point $y$ in the boundary of $\bar{Y}$ where $y_2 = 2$, and so forth. Given the point $(y_1, y_3) = (-1, -1)$ where the maximum possible output of commodity 2 is one unit, it is possible to find a point $y^*$ in $\bar{Y}$ such that $y_1^* < y_1$, $y_2^* \geqq y_2$ and $y_3^* > y_3$, namely the point $a = (y_1^*, y_3^*) = (-\frac{7}{4}, -\frac{2}{4})$ in Figure 4.1 where

$y_2^* = 1$. Also given the point $(-1, -1)$ where the maximum possible output of commodity 2 is one unit, it is possible to find a point $y^*$ in $\bar{Y}$ such that $y_1^* > y_1$, $y_2^* \geqq y_2$, and $y_3^* < y_3$, namely the point $b = (y_1^*, y_3^*) = (-\frac{1}{2}, -\frac{3}{2})$ where $y_2^* = 1$. This demonstrates that indirect substitutability with respect to $Y$ implies direct substitutability with respect to $\bar{Y}$.

Instead of writing out the words "commodity $j$ is an indirect substitute for commodity $k$," we may define the substitution relation $S$.

DEFINITION 4.2.3. The relation $S$ between two commodities $j$ and $k$, which is written $j\ S\ k$, holds if commodity $j$ is an indirect substitute for commodity $k$.

Any relation $S$ is symmetric if $j\ S\ k$ implies $k\ S\ j$. It is not necessarily true that if commodity $j$ is an indirect substitute for commodity $k$, then commodity $k$ is an indirect substitute for commodity $j$. Thus the relation $S$ is not symmetric.

Any relation $S$ is reflexive if $j\ S\ j$. By examination of our definition of weak or indirect substitutability (Definition 4.2.2), we see that a commodity cannot be a substitute for itself. Thus the relation $S$ is not reflexive.

The relation $S$ is transitive if $h\ S\ j$ and $j\ S\ k$ imply that $h\ S\ k$. We may prove that the relation $S$ is transitive.

THEOREM 4.2.1. *Given Postulate A (additivity), the relation S is transitive.*

*Proof:* Suppose we are given the possible point $y$. Without loss of generality, we may assume that $1\ S\ 2$ and $2\ S\ 3$. We will show that this implies that $1\ S\ 3$. Since commodity 1 is a substitute for commodity 2, there exists a positive integer $\lambda_1$ and a possible point $y^*$ such that

$$\begin{aligned} y_1^* &= \lambda_1 \cdot y_1 - \alpha_{11} \\ y_i^* &= \lambda_1 \cdot y_i + \alpha_{i1} \quad \text{for} \quad i = 2, \ldots, n \end{aligned} \tag{4.2.1}$$

where

$$\begin{aligned} \alpha_{i1} &\geqq 0 \quad \text{for} \quad i = 1, \ldots, n \\ \alpha_{i1} &> 0 \quad \text{for} \quad i = 1 \quad \text{and} \quad i = 2 \end{aligned} \tag{4.2.2}$$

Similarly, since commodity 2 is a substitute for commodity 3, there exists a positive integer $\lambda_2$ and a possible point $y^{**}$ such that

$$\begin{aligned} y_2^{**} &= \lambda_2 \cdot y_2 - \alpha_{22} \\ y_i^{**} &= \lambda_2 \cdot y_i + \alpha_{i2} \quad \text{for} \quad i = 1 \quad \text{and} \quad i = 3, \ldots, n \end{aligned} \tag{4.2.3}$$

where

$$\begin{aligned} \alpha_{i2} &\geqq 0 \quad \text{for} \quad i = 1, \ldots, n \\ \alpha_{i2} &> 0 \quad \text{for} \quad i = 2 \quad \text{and} \quad i = 3 \end{aligned} \tag{4.2.4}$$

Let $t$ be an arbitrarily large integer. The point $t\cdot y^*$ belongs to $Y$ because of additivity, which also implies that $\bar{y} = t\cdot y^* + y^{**}$ belongs to $Y$. From (4.2.1) and (4.2.3), we have

$$\begin{aligned} \bar{y}_1 &= (t\cdot\lambda_1 + \lambda_2)\cdot y_1 + (-t\cdot\alpha_{11} + \alpha_{12}) \\ \bar{y}_2 &= (t\cdot\lambda_1 + \lambda_2)\cdot y_2 + (t\cdot\alpha_{21} - \alpha_{22}) \\ \bar{y}_i &= (t\cdot\lambda_1 + \lambda_2)\cdot y_i + (t\alpha_{i1} + \alpha_{i2}) \end{aligned} \tag{4.2.5}$$

Since $t$ is an arbitrarily large integer, from (4.2.2) and (4.2.4) we have

$$\begin{aligned} -t\cdot\alpha_{11} + \alpha_{12} &< 0 \\ t\cdot\alpha_{21} - \alpha_{22} &> 0 \\ t\cdot\alpha_{31} + \alpha_{32} &> 0 \\ t\cdot\alpha_{i1} + \alpha_{i2} &\geqq 0 \quad \text{for} \quad i = 4,\ldots,n. \end{aligned} \tag{4.2.6}$$

Since there exist a possible point $\bar{y}$ and an integer $(t\cdot\lambda_1 + \lambda_2)$ which satisfy (4.2.5) and (4.2.6), it follows that $1\,S\,3$ and the relation $S$ is transitive.

This means that if commodity $h$ is an indirect substitute for commodity $j$ and commodity $j$ is an indirect substitute for commodity $k$, then commodity $h$ is an indirect substitute for commodity $k$. This result seems intuitively obvious. The next theorem, however, is not so obvious.

THEOREM 4.2.2. *Given Postulates A (additivity), B (inaction), C (disposal), D (closure), and E (integer convexity), if a commodity is an indirect substitute for every input (except perhaps itself), then that commodity is also an indirect substitute for every output (except perhaps itself). If a commodity is an indirect substitute for every output (except perhaps itself), then that commodity is an indirect substitute for every input (except perhaps itself).*

*Proof:* Without loss of generality, we may assume that commodity $n$ is an indirect substitute for all inputs given the possible point $y^*$. Also without loss of generality, let us assume that commodities $i = 1,\ldots,n_1$ are inputs $(y_i^* < 0)$, commodities $i = n_1 + 1,\ldots,n_2$ are outputs $(y_i^* > 0)$, and for $i = n_2 + 1,\ldots,n - 1$, $y_i^* = 0$. Since commodity $n$ is an indirect substitute for commodities $i = 1,\ldots,n_1$, there exist positive integers $\lambda_1, \lambda_2,\ldots,\lambda_{n_1}$ and possible points $y^j = (y_{1j}, y_{2j},\ldots, y_{nj})$ for $j = 1,\ldots,n_1$ such that

$$\begin{aligned} y_{nj} &< \lambda_j\cdot y_n^* \\ y_{ij} &\geqq \lambda_j\cdot y_i^* \quad \text{for} \quad i = 1,\ldots,n-1 \\ y_{jj} &> \lambda_j\cdot y_j^* \end{aligned} \tag{4.2.7}$$

for $j = 1,\ldots,n_1$. Since $\bar{Y}$ is a convex cone with vertex the origin (Theorem 2.9.1), and since $y^j$ is contained in $Y$, the points $y^j/\lambda_j$ belong to $\bar{Y}$ for $j = 1, \ldots, n_1$. The co-ordinates may be written as follows:

$$\begin{aligned} y_{nj}/\lambda_j &= y_n^* - \alpha_{nj} \\ y_{ij}/\lambda_j &= y_i^* + \alpha_{ij} \quad \text{for} \quad i = 1, \ldots, n-1 \end{aligned} \tag{4.2.8}$$

where

$$\begin{aligned} \alpha_{ij} &\geqq 0 \quad \text{for} \quad i = 1, \ldots, n \\ \alpha_{jj} &> 0 \\ \alpha_{nj} &> 0 \end{aligned} \tag{4.2.9}$$

for $j = 1, \ldots, n_1$. The numbers $y_{ij}$ and $\lambda_j \cdot y_i^*$ differ by an integer if $i \in D$ where $D$ is the set of indivisible commodities (Postulate $E$). Thus $\alpha_{ij}$ is a rational number if $i \in D$.

Let $\sum_{j=1}^{n_1} t_j = 1$ and assume that $t_j > 0$ for $j = 1, \ldots, n_1$. Then $y^{**} = \sum_{j=1}^{n_1} t_j \cdot (y^j/\lambda_j)$ is a point of $\bar{Y}$. The co-ordinates of $y^{**}$ may be written as

$$y_n^{**} = y_n^* - \sum_{j=1}^{n_1} t_j \cdot \alpha_{nj} = y_n^* - \gamma_n$$

$$y_i^{**} = y_i^* + \sum_{j=1}^{n_1} t_j \cdot \alpha_{ij} = y_i^* + \gamma_i \qquad \text{for} \quad i = 1, \ldots, n-1. \tag{4.2.10}$$

Since $t_j > 0$ for $j = 1, \ldots, n_1$, from (4.2.9) we have

$$\gamma_i \geqq 0 \quad \text{for} \quad 1, \ldots, n$$

and

$$\gamma_i > 0 \quad \text{for} \quad 1, \ldots, n_1. \tag{4.2.11}$$

Let

$$\lambda^* = \min_{i=1,\ldots,n_1} \left( \frac{-\gamma_i}{y_i^*} \right). \tag{4.2.12}$$

From (4.2.11) we see that

$$\lambda^* > 0. \tag{4.2.13}$$

Let $\lambda$ be a rational scalar where

$$0 < \lambda \leqq \lambda^* \leqq \frac{-\gamma_i}{y_i^*} \quad \text{for} \quad i = 1, \ldots, n_1. \tag{4.2.14}$$

The point $(1 + \lambda) \cdot y^{**}$ belongs to $\bar{Y}$ because $\bar{Y}$ is a convex cone with vertex the origin. Multiply both sides of the inequality $\lambda \leqq -\gamma_i/y_i^*$ by $y_i^*$ (where $y_i^*$ is negative for $i = 1, \ldots, n_1$) to obtain $\lambda \cdot y_i^* \geqq -\gamma_i$. Add $y_i^* + \gamma_i$ to both sides of this inequality and add $\lambda \cdot \gamma_i$ to the left hand side of this inequality (where from (4.2.14) and (4.2.11), it follows that $\lambda \cdot \gamma_i \geqq 0$) to obtain

$$(1 + \lambda) \cdot y_i^{**} = (1 + \lambda) \cdot (y_i^* + \gamma_i) \geqq y_i^* \quad \text{for} \quad i = 1, \ldots, n_1. \tag{4.2.15}$$

On the other hand, since $y_i^* > 0$, $\gamma_i \geqq 0$, and $\lambda > 0$ for $i = n_1 + 1, \ldots, n_2$, we have

$$(1 + \lambda) \cdot y_i^{**} = (1 + \lambda) \cdot (y_i^* + \gamma_i) > y_i^* \quad \text{for} \quad i = n_1 + 1, \ldots, n_2. \tag{4.2.16}$$

Since $y_i^* = 0$, $\gamma_i \geqq 0$, and $\lambda > 0$ for $i = n_2 + 1, \ldots, n - 1$, it follows that

$$(1 + \lambda) \cdot y_i^{**} = (1 + \lambda) \cdot (y_i^* + \gamma_i) \geqq y_i^* \quad \text{for} \quad i = n_2 + 1, \ldots, n - 1. \tag{4.2.17}$$

The inequalities (4.2.15), (4.2.16), and (4.2.17) may be summed up as follows

$$(1 + \lambda) \cdot y^{**} = y^* + (\delta_1, \delta_2, \ldots, \delta_n) \tag{4.2.18}$$

where

$$\begin{aligned} &\delta_i \geqq 0 \quad \text{for} \quad i = 1, \ldots, n - 1 \\ &\delta_i > 0 \quad \text{for} \quad i = n_1 + 1, \ldots, n_2. \end{aligned} \tag{4.2.19}$$

Since $y_i^*$ is integer for all $i$ in $D$, the set of indivisible commodities (Postulate E), since $\lambda$ is rational, and since $y_i$ is rational for all $i$ in $D$, $\delta_i$ is rational for all $i$ in $D$. Hence we may write

$$\delta_i = \frac{\bar{\delta}_i}{\delta} \quad \text{for} \quad i \text{ in } D \tag{4.2.20}$$

where $\delta$ is the least common denominator of all the fractions $\delta_i$ for $i$ contained in $D$. Then

$$y^0 = \delta \cdot (1 + \lambda) \cdot y^{**} = \delta y^* + (\beta_1, \beta_2, \ldots, \beta_n) \tag{4.2.21}$$

where

$$\beta_i = \bar{\delta}_i \text{ for } i \text{ contained in } D. \tag{4.2.22}$$

Since $\delta > 0$, $y^0$ belongs to $\bar{Y}$ because $\bar{Y}$ is a convex cone with vertex the origin. Since $\beta_i$ is integer for all $i$ contained in $D$, $y^0$ is possible (Postulate E). Let commodity $k$ be an output. Then from equations (4.2.19) and (4.2.22) we see that

$$\begin{aligned} &\beta_k > 0 \\ &\beta_i \geqq 0 \quad \text{for} \quad i = 1, \ldots, n - 1. \end{aligned} \tag{4.2.23}$$

Furthermore if $\beta_n \geqq 0$, we may always dispose enough units of commodity $n$ so that we may express a possible point $y^0$ in terms of $y^*$ as in (4.2.21) where (4.2.23) is satisfied and where

$$\beta_n < 0 \tag{4.2.24}$$

The existence of a possible point $y^0$ which satisfies (4.2.21), (4.2.23), and (4.2.24) implies that commodity $n$ is an indirect substitute for commodity $k$ where commodity $k$ is any output. Thus if any commodity is an indirect substitute for all inputs then that commodity is an indirect substitute for every output. If a commodity is an indirect substitute for all outputs, then we may use a proof which is very similar.

Although the above proof is rather cumbersome, the reasoning behind it is quite simple. Let us consider the case where an input is an indirect substitute for all other inputs. Then for a sufficient increase in scale, it is possible to use more (in absolute value) of that input along with less (in absolute value) of every other input while producing no less of every output. On the other hand for an even larger increase in scale, it is possible to sacrific some but not all of the savings in all the other inputs to produce more of any output instead.

## 4.3 Discriminatory Pricing

The term discriminatory pricing refers to the way in which profit is calculated. Profit is not defined, as in Chapter 2, as the vector product of a price vector and a possible point but is assumed to be a summation or an integration of vector products, depending on whether we are concerned with discrete or continuous functions.

We assume that the price system $p(y)$ for $y \in Y$ is independent. That is, we assume that the function $p(y)$ of the vector $y$ can be defined in terms of the separate functions $p_i(y_i)$ for $i = 1, \ldots, n$ where $y_i$ is the $i^{\text{th}}$ coordinate of a possible point $y$. With an independent price system, the price of the $j^{\text{th}}$ commodity is dependent on the amount $y_j$ of the $j^{\text{th}}$ commodity and is independent of the amounts of the other commodities $i \neq j$.

Now for each $y \in Y$, we have the function $p(y) = (p_1(y_1), \ldots, p_n(y_n))$. If the $i^{\text{th}}$ commodity is indivisible $y \in Y$, implies that $y_i$ is integer. Thus, if the $i^{\text{th}}$ commodity is indivisible, the function $p_i(y_i)$ is defined only for integer $y_i$. We extend the domain of definition in the following manner:
Let $y_i = [y_i] + \{y_i\}$ where $\{y_i\}$ is the non-negative fractional part of $y_i$, and $[y_i]$ is the integer part of $y_i$. Then

$$p_i(y_i) = \begin{cases} p_i([y_i] + 1) & \text{if } \{y_i\} > 0 \\ p_i([y_i]) & \text{if } \{y_i\} = 0. \end{cases} \tag{4.3.1}$$

Let $\int_0^{y_i^*} p_i(y_i)\, dy_i$ be the integral of the function $p_i(y_i)$ over the interval from 0 to $y_i^*$.

Profit of a possible point $y^*$ is defined as the sum of $n$ integrals

DEFINITION 4.3.1. Profit $\pi(y^*)$ of the possible point $y^*$ with discriminatory pricing is defined as

$$\pi(y^*) = \sum_{i=1}^{n} \int_0^{y_i^*} p_i(y_i)\, dy_i. \tag{4.3.2}$$

Now if $y_i^* \geqq 0$, then since $p_i(y_i) \geqq 0$, the integral $\int_0^{y_i^*} p_i(y_i)\, dy_i \geqq 0$. That is, if for a particular possible point the $i^{\text{th}}$ commodity is an output, then the $\int_0^{y_i^*} p_i(y_i)\, dy_i \geqq 0$ and this quantity is referred to as a revenue. If $y_i^* \leqq 0$, then $-\int_0^{y_i^*} p_i(y_i)\, dy_i \geqq 0$ is termed a cost. Thus with discriminatory pricing profit is the sum of revenues less the sum of costs.

Now if there are two possible points $y'$ and $y''$, the profit of the point $y''$ may be expressed in terms of the profit of the point $y'$ as follows:

$$\pi(y'') = \pi(y') + \sum_{i=1}^{n} \int_{y_i'}^{y_i''} p_i(y_i)\, dy_i. \tag{4.3.3}$$

In particular, if $y' = 0$ (inaction) then $\pi(0) = 0$, and

$$\pi(y'') = \pi(0) + \sum_{i=1}^{n} \int_0^{y_i''} p_i(y_i)\, dy_i. \tag{4.3.4}$$

Suppose $p_i(y_i) = p_i$, a constant, for all $y_i$ in the interval $0 \leqq y_i \leqq y_i''$, if $y_i'' \geqq 0$ or in the interval $y_i'' \leqq y_i < 0$, if $y_i'' < 0$. Then each of the integrals $\int_0^{y_i''} p_i(y_i)\, dy_i = \int_0^{y_i''} p_i \cdot dy_i$ reduces to $p_i \cdot y_i''$ and the sum

$$\sum_{i=1}^{n} \int_0^{y_i''} p_i(y_i)\, dy_i = \sum_{i=1}^{n} \int_0^{y_i''} p_i \cdot dy_i$$

reduces to $p \cdot y''$ where $p = (p_1, p_2, \ldots, p_n)$. In particular, if the price system $p(y)$ is competitive ($p(y) = p$ for all $y \in Y$), then the profit of any point $y \in Y$ is $p \cdot y$. Thus profit with discriminatory pricing reduces to our previous definition of profit in Chapter 2 whenever the pricing system is competitive.

To illustrate, let us consider Figure 4.3. The vertical axis represents the function $p_i(y_i)$; the horizontal axis represents the amount $y_i$ of the $i^{\text{th}}$ commodity. The $i^{\text{th}}$ commodity is assumed to be indivisible. Originally the function $p_i(y_i)$ is defined only for integer $y_i$, i.e., $p_i(y_i)$ is defined only for 0, 1, 2, etc., and $-1$, $-2$, $-3$, etc. In terms of Figure 4.3, originally $p_i(y_i)$ is defined only at points indicated by the heavy dots. We may extend the domain of definition as in equation (4.3.1) by defining $p_i(y_i)$ where $y_i$ is not an integer as equal to $p_i(y_i^*)$ for the smallest integer $y_i^*$ which is

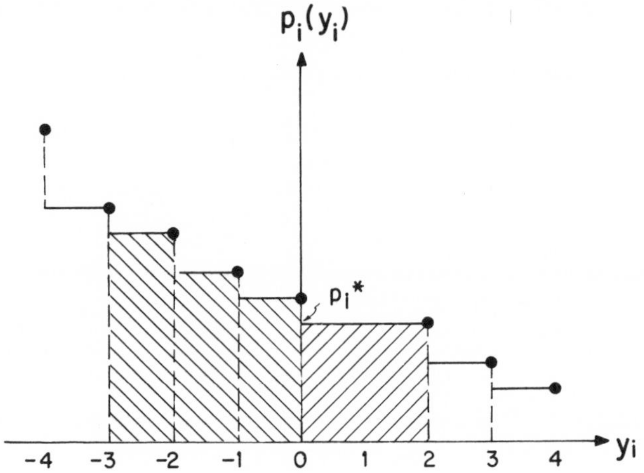


Figure 4.3

larger than $y_i$. For example, $p_i(-\frac{3}{2}) = p(-1)$ and $p(\frac{7}{3}) = p(3)$. In terms of Figure 4.3, the function $p_i(y_i)$ over the extended domain of definition is represented by the horizontal line segments which have the heavy dots at their right hand terminals.

If $y_i < 0$ then the $i^{\text{th}}$ commodity is an input. Suppose $y_i = -3$. Then the integral $\int_0^{-3} p_i(y_i)\, dy_i$ is represented by the shaded area to the left of the vertical axis in Figure 4.3. This integral is negative, i.e., the input $y_i = -3$ gives rise to a cost. If $y_i > 0$, then the $i^{\text{th}}$ commodity is an output. Suppose $y_i = 2$. Then the integral $\int_0^2 p_i(y_i)\, dy_i$ is equivalent to the shaded area to the right of the vertical axis in Figure 4.3. This integral is positive, i.e., the output $y_i = 2$ gives rise to a revenue. Since the price $p_i(y_i)$ is a constant $p_i^*$ over the interval $0 < y_i \leqq 2$, the integral $\int_0^2 p_i(y_i)\, dy_i$ reduces to $p_i^*(2 - 0) = p_i^* \cdot 2$.

## 4.4 Profit Maximization and Discriminatory Pricing

With discriminatory pricing, we define a profit-maximizing possible point in the usual fashion.

DEFINITION 4.4.1. If $y^* \in Y$ and $\pi(y^*) \geqq \pi(y)$ for all $y \in Y$, then $y^*$ is a profit-maximizing possible point with discriminatory pricing.

Several of the theorems which were derived concerning profit maximization where profit is a vector product (Definition 2.11.1) must be modified when profit is computed on the basis of discriminatory pricing. One of these theorems (Theorem 2.11.2) is that maximum profits are zero if a profit-maximizing possible point exists. With discriminatory pricing, maximum profits may be positive but not negative, given the inaction postulate (Postulate B).

THEOREM 4.4.1. *Given Postulate B (inaction), if a profit-maximizing possible point $y^*$ exists with discriminatory pricing, then $\pi(y^*) \geqq 0$.*
*Proof:* Since $\pi(0) = 0$, we have $\pi(y^*) \geqq \pi(0) = 0$.

When profit is defined as a vector product (Definition 2.11.1), any profit-maximizing input-output combination is efficient (Theorem 2.12.2). The same holds true with discriminatory pricing.

THEOREM 4.4.2. *A profit-maximizing point $y^* \in Y$ with a positive discriminatory pricing system $p(y) > 0$ is efficient.*
*Proof:* Suppose $y^*$ were not efficient, i.e., there exists a $y^{**} \in Y$ such that $y_i^{**} \geqq y_i^*$ for all $i$ and $y_i > y_i^*$ for at least one $i$.

$$\pi(y) = \pi(y^*) + \sum_{i=1}^{n} \int_{y_i^*}^{y_i^{**}} p_i(y_i)\, dy_i \tag{4.4.1}$$

Now $y_i^{**} \geqq y_i^*$ for all $i$ and $y_i^{**} > y_i^*$ for at least one $i$. Also $p_i(y_i) > 0$ for all $i$. Thus

$$\sum_{i=1}^{n} \int_{y_i^*}^{y_i^{**}} p_i(y_i)\, dy_i > 0 \tag{4.4.2}$$

Hence $\pi(y) > \pi(y^*)$, and $y^*$ is not profit-maximizing.

While the converse of Theorem 2.12.1 is not true, the converse of Theorem 4.4.1 is true. That is, as we shall demonstrate later (Chapter 5), given an efficient point $y^*$ we can always find a system of discriminatory prices such that $y^*$ is profit-maximizing.

## 4.5 Conclusion

The notion of discriminatory pricing introduced in this chapter does not necessarily correspond in all respects to traditional notions of discriminatory price behavior. We are not concerned with the manner in which a system of discriminatory pricing is enforced in an exchange market. In our theory, a discriminatory price mechanism is specified by a price-quantity relationship which an economic agent accepts as given to him and by a calculation of revenues and costs in a way which presumes that successive units of commodities are purchased or sold at different prices.

Neither are we concerned with precisely who buys what output at what price or who sells what input at what price. The economic agent sells successive units of output at various prices, but to whom is no concern of ours in this theory. In the case of an inverse pricing system, the first units sold are sold at a higher price (or a price no lower) than later units. As far as the agent is concerned, the buyers are served on a first come-first served basis. Thus we are not directly concerned (in our pure theory) with questions of discrimination by location or by different classes of buyers.[2]

[2] For a discussion of these questions see J. M. Clark, *Studies in the Economics of Overhead Costs* (Chicago: University of Chicago Press, 1923), pp. 416–433. See also Joan V. Robinson, *Economics of Imperfect Competition* (New York: St. Martin's Press, 1961), pp. 179–208; K. E. Boulding, op.cit., pp. 540–556; and Erich Schneider, *Pricing and Equilibrium* (New York: Macmillan Co., 1962).

# CHAPTER 5

## *ATTAINING EFFICIENCY*

### 5.1 Introduction

Suppose the attainable point $z^* = r + y^*$ is a profit-maximizing attainable point. Then $y^*$ is an efficient possible point. The central question with which this chapter is concerned is the existence of a positive price vector $p > 0$ such that $y^*$ is a profit-maximizing *possible* point. The resource limitations must be considered explicitly in arriving at a profit-maximizing *attainable* point $z^* = r + y^*$. Resource limitations are ignored if $y^*$ can be made profit-maximizing for some vector $p > 0$. This is the essence of decentralized decision making, the prices $p$ reflect resource scarcities so that profit maximization can take place without explicit consideration of such scarcities. With regard to the existence of such prices, we shall see that the notions of constant returns and substitutability play a very important role.

This chapter has a second objective, however. Proof of several theorems suggest various mechanisms other than profit maximization with a given set of prices which will ensure that all efficient points are profit-maximizing. With regard to this objective, Theorem 5.4.1 shows that for each efficient point, there exists a competitive price system such that the loss of that efficient point does not exceed some finite limit. This suggests that when increasing returns to scale prevail, a subsidy might be paid to make up for the loss. The subsidy need never exceed some finite amount. Furthermore, one can show that if the scale of operations is sufficiently large, losses are an insignificant proportion of total revenue or of total cost (Corollary 5.4.16). We may postulate that if losses are small enough relative to total revenue, then an economic agent disregards them. In this way the efficient point $y^*$ will be attainable as profit "sufficing." That is, profits will be sufficiently close to maximum profits to suit the economic agent. Similarly, we show (Corollary 5.4.1b) that any efficient attainable point $z^*$ is "almost" profit-maximizing. Finally, Theorem 5.5.1 shows that for each efficient point $y^*$, there exists a particularly simple price system such that $y^*$ and the efficient point $z^* = r + y^*$ are profit-maximizing with discriminatory pricing.

Throughout this chapter we shall refer to the following Fundamental Theorem:

FUNDAMENTAL THEOREM. *Let $\bar{Y}$ be a closed convex cone. The point $y^*$ is efficient with respect to $\bar{Y}$. Let $A$, the local possible cone, be the set of points $t \cdot (y - y^*)$ where the scalar $t > 0$ and $y \in \bar{Y}$. Let $(A)$ be the closure of $A$. Then there exists a price vector $p > 0$ such that $p \cdot y^* \geqq p \cdot y$ for all $y \in Y$.*

(*a*) *if and only if* $y^*$ *is efficient with respect to the translation* $y^* + (A)$; *or*

(*b*) *if* $\bar{Y}$ *is polyhedral; or*

(*c*) *if* $y^* \in \bar{Y}$ *and for all* $i$ *the* $i^{\text{th}}$ *commodity is an indirect substitute for all outputs (resp. inputs) except itself.*

The sufficiency condition (*b*) has been proved by Koopmans and Gale.[1] The necessary and sufficient condition (*a*) and the sufficient condition (*c*) are proved in the appendix along with a restatement of the essentials of the Koopman's proof.

The Fundamental Theorem shows that the converse of the efficiency theorem (Theorem 2.12.1) is true if and only if $y^*$ is also efficient with respect to $y^* + (A)$. This condition may be called a strict efficiency criterion. It essentially rules out cases where in the terminology of more conventional production theory, the marginal rates of transformation among outputs are zero or the marginal rates of substitution among inputs are zero. To see how a violation of (*a*) can result, note Figure 5.1. This is the cross section of a three-dimensional set $Y$ of production possibilities where the third co-ordinate $y_3^*$ is fixed at some negative value. The set $A$ is called the local possible cone and is generated by drawing a ray from $y^*$ through every point $y$ in the set $Y$. The set $A$ in Figure 5.1 refers to the set of points to the left of the line *ECD* but not including the positive portion *EC*. The closure $(A)$, of course, includes the whole line *ECD*. The point $y^0$ lies in $y^* + (A)$ and $y_1^0 > y_1^*$ with $y_2^0 = y_2^*$ so that $y^*$ is not efficient with respect to $y^* + (A)$. The point $y^*$ is efficient, however, with respect to $Y$. On the other hand there is no positive price vector such that $y^*$ is profit-maximizing. The only price vector that makes $y^*$ profit-maximizing is the vector $p$ which is perpendicular to the line *ECD* which requires the price $p_2$ be equal to 0.

## 5.2 Constant Returns

In Chapter 3 we showed that Postulates A (additivity) and B (inaction) imply that all efficient points could be placed in one of two categories. Either an efficient point exhibits constant returns for increases in scale or it exhibits increasing returns. Theorem 3.6.1 states that if an efficient point $y^*$ exhibits increasing returns, then there exists no competitive price system such that $y^*$ is a profit-maximizing possible point. We shall now show that Postulates A, B, C, D, and E imply that if a *strictly* efficient point $y^*$ exhibits constant returns for increases in scale, there also exists a competitive price system such that $y^*$ is a profit-maximizing possible point.

[1] Theorem 4.3 in T. C. Koopmans' "Analysis of Production as an Efficient Combination of Activities" ed. T. C. Koopmans, *Activity Analysis of Production and Allocation* (New York: Wiley, 1951), pp. 61–63. See also D. Gale, *The Theory of Linear Economic Models* (New York: McGraw Hill, 1960), pp. 308–311.

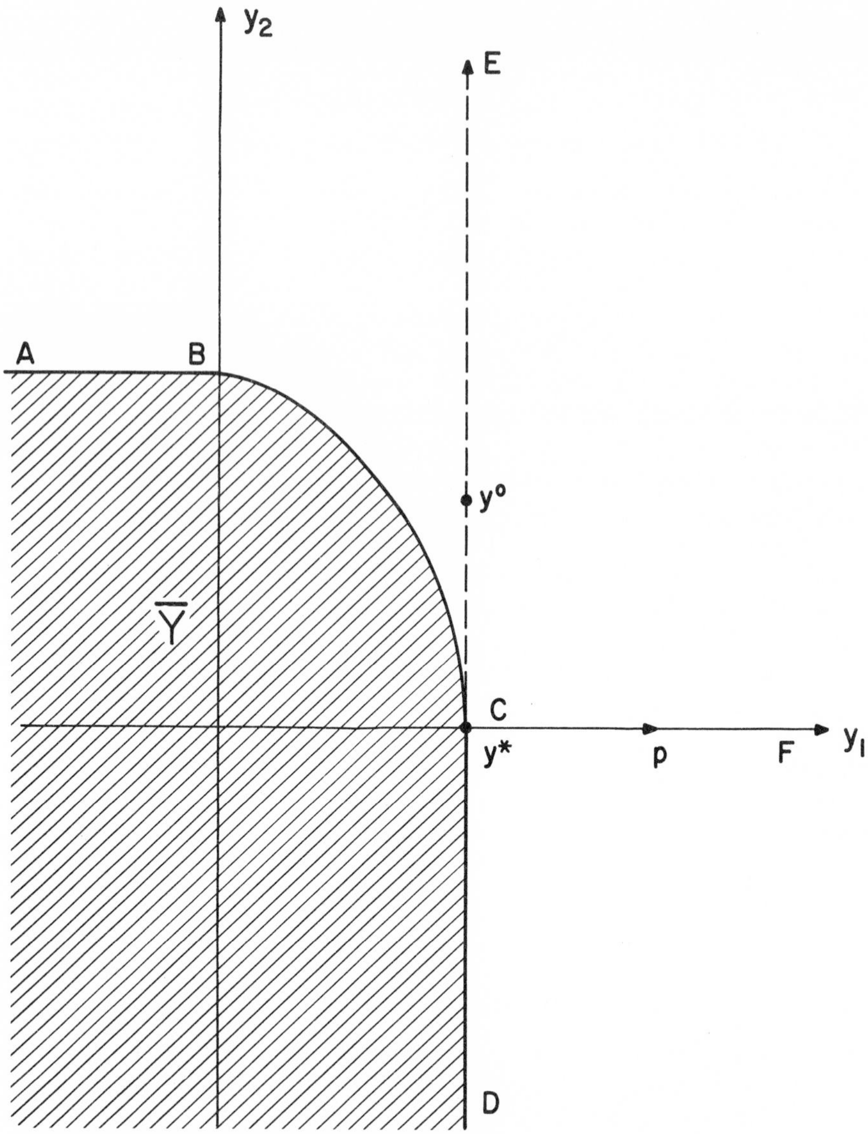


**Figure 5.1**

THEOREM 5.2.1. *Given Postulate A (additivity), B (inaction), C (disposal), D (closure), and E (integer convexity), if the possible point $y^*$ exhibits constant returns for increase in scale and if (a), (b) or (c) of the Fundamental Theorem applies, then there exists a competitive price vector $p > 0$ such that $y^*$ is a profit maximizing possible point.*

*Proof:* According to Theorem 2.9.1, $\bar{Y}$ is a closed convex cone and from Theorem 3.6.2, $y^*$ is efficient with respect to $\bar{Y}$, which is all we need to show.

In Figure 5.2 the convex hull of $Y$ is the shaded area. The set $Y$ itself consists of the heavy dots within the shaded area. The point $y^*$ is both efficient and efficient with respect to $\bar{Y}$. That is, there are no points of $Y$ and no points of $\bar{Y}$ above and to the right of $y^*$. The point $y^*$ exhibits constant returns for integer changes in scale (Theorem 3.6.2). The point $y^*$ also lies in the boundary of $\bar{Y}$, the convex hull of $Y$. Since $\bar{Y}$ is polyhedral, Theorem 5.2.1 is equivalent to the statement that there exists a supporting hyperplane through the point $y^*$. This supporting hyperplane is the line $AB$ in Figure 5.2. The price vector $p$ is normal (perpendicular) to this hyperplane. Since $y^*$ lies in the hyperplane, the hyperplane contains all points $y$ where $p \cdot y = p \cdot y^*$. For any point $y^*$ which lies above and to the right of the hyperplane $AB$, we have $p \cdot y > p \cdot y^*$. Any point above and to the right of the hyperplane $AB$ is not a point of $Y$. Thus if $y$ is a point of $Y$, it must lie on or below and to the left of the hyperplane $AB$, i.e., $p \cdot y \leqq p \cdot y^*$. Thus $y^*$ is profit-maximizing, given the price vector $p$.

On the other hand, both the points $y^{**}$ and $y^0$ are efficient, but neither is efficient with respect to $\bar{Y}$. There are no points of $Y$ above and to the right of either $y^{**}$ or $y^0$, but there are points of $\bar{Y}$ above and to the right of both $y^{**}$ and $y^0$. The points $y^{**}$ and $y^0$ exhibit increasing returns rather than constant returns. Neither lies in the boundary of $\bar{Y}$. There is no supporting hyperplane either through the point $y^{**}$ or through the point $y^0$.

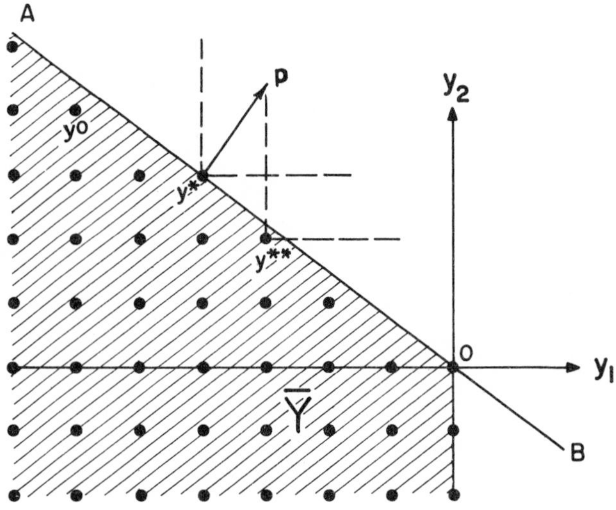


Figure 5.2

Figure 5.3 pictures the attainable set $Z$ derived from the set $Y$ of production possibilities. The shaded area represents the convex hull of the set $Z$. The set $Z$ consists of the heavy dots within the shaded area. The point $z^* = r + y^*$ is a profit-maximizing attainable point given the price vector $p$ since $y^*$ exhibits constant returns. There is no price vector $p$ for which $z^{**} = r + y^{**}$ is a profit-maximizing attainable point. On the other hand, $z^0 = r + y^0$ is a profit-maximizing attainable point given the positive price vector $p'$ even though $y^0$ exhibits increasing returns. If a possible point $y$ exhibits constant returns and is strictly efficient, there is always a guarantee that there exists a positive price vector $p$ such that $z = r + y$ is a profit-maximizing attainable point. If $y$ exhibits increasing returns, there may or may not be a positive price vector $p$ such that $z = r + y$ is a profit-maximizing attainable point. In any case if $y$ exhibits increasing returns there definitely is not a positive price vector such that $y$ is a profit-maximizing possible point.

## 5.3 Substitution

THEOREM 5.3.1. *Given Postulates A (additivity), B (inaction), C (disposal), D (closure), and E (integer convexity), if every indivisible commodity is an indirect substitute for a divisible commodity and if (a), (b) or (c) of the Fundamental Theorem applies, then there exists a competitive price vector $p > 0$ such that an efficient point $y^* \in Y$ is a profit maximizing possible point.*

*Proof:* We shall demonstrate that if $y^*$ is efficient, then $y^*$ is efficient with respect to $\bar{Y}$. Suppose $y^*$ is not efficient with respect to $\bar{Y}$. Then

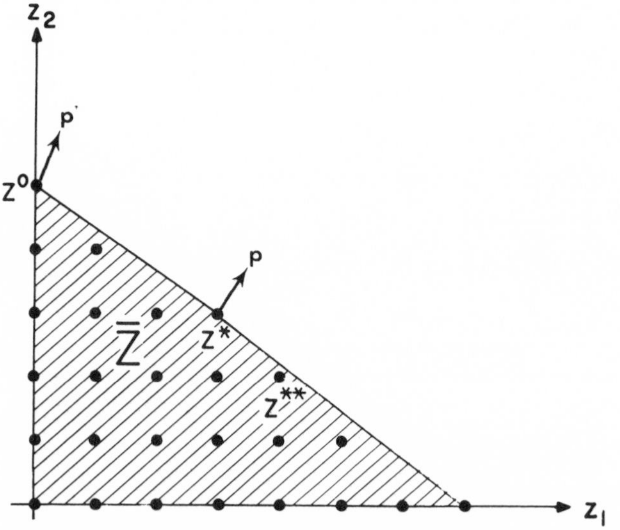


Figure 5.3

there exists a point $y \in \bar{Y}$ such that $y \geq y^*$. Let us assume (without loss of generality) that $y_1 > y_1^*$. Then

$$y = y^* + \beta \tag{5.3.1}$$

where

$$\begin{aligned} &\beta_1 > 0 \\ &\beta_i \geqq 0 \quad \text{for} \quad i = 2, \ldots, n. \end{aligned} \tag{5.3.2}$$

We may assume (also without loss of generality) that commodity 2 is a divisible commodity. Then suppose that commodity 1 is an indirect substitute for commodity 2. This means that there exists an integer $\lambda$ where $\lambda > 0$ and a point $y^{**}$ such that

$$\begin{aligned} &y_1^{**} < \lambda \cdot y_1^* \\ &y_2^{**} > \lambda \cdot y_2^* \\ &y_i^{**} \geqq \lambda \cdot y_i^* \quad \text{for} \quad i = 3, \ldots, n. \end{aligned} \tag{5.3.3}$$

Since $\bar{Y}$ is a convex cone with vertex the origin, the point $y^{**}/\lambda$ belongs to $\bar{Y}$. Now

$$y^{**}/\lambda = y^* + \alpha \tag{5.3.4}$$

where

$$\begin{aligned} &\alpha_1 < 0 \\ &\alpha_2 > 0 \\ &\alpha_i \geqq 0 \quad \text{for} \quad i = 3, \ldots, n \end{aligned} \tag{5.3.5}$$

Let $t = \alpha_1/(\alpha_1 - \beta_1)$. From the inequalities in (5.3.2) and (5.3.5), we see that $0 < t < 1$. Then $y^0 = t \cdot y + (1 - t)y^{**}/\lambda$ is a convex combination of $y$ and $y^{**}/\lambda$ which both belong to $\bar{Y}$. Thus $y^0$ belongs to $\bar{Y}$. From (5.3.1) and (5.3.4), we have

$$\begin{aligned} &y_1^0 = y_1^* \\ &y_i^0 = y_1^* + \frac{\beta_1 \cdot \alpha_i - \alpha_1 \cdot \beta_i}{\beta_1 - \alpha_1} \quad \text{for} \quad i = 2, \ldots, n \end{aligned} \tag{5.3.6}$$

where

$$\gamma_i = \frac{\beta_1 \cdot \alpha_i - \alpha_1 \cdot \beta_i}{\beta_1 - \alpha_1} \begin{cases} > 0 & \text{if} \quad i = 2 \\ \geqq 0 & \text{if} \quad i = 3, \ldots, n. \end{cases} \tag{5.3.7}$$

According to Theorem 2.9.2, the point $y^{00} = (y_1^*, y_2^* + \gamma_2, y_3^*, \ldots, y_n^*)$ belongs to $\bar{Y}$. Furthermore since commodity 2 is divisible, the point $y^{00}$ belongs to $Y$ (Postulate E). Now $y^{00} \geq y^*$ and thus $y^*$ is not efficient. This is a contradiction; thus $y^*$ is efficient with respect to $\bar{Y}$.

The proof of the above theorem may be explained in an informal way. First of all, given that every indivisible input is a substitute for a divisible commodity, if a unit of an indivisible input is used to less than full capacity or if a unit of an indivisible output is completed only partially, then efficiency has not been achieved. One can always use some of the excess capacity of a unit of an indivisible input and employ less of a divisible input or produce more of a divisible output. That is, in a sense we substitute the excess capacity for a divisible input or output and arrive at a more efficient situation. Similarly, one may always less than fully complete a unit of an indivisible output and use less of a divisible input or produce more of a divisible output. In other words, we may substitute the partial completion of a unit of an indivisible output for a divisible output or divisible input to achieve greater efficiency. Since the only efficient situation is one in which all units of all indivisible inputs are fully utilized and all units of all indivisible outputs are fully completed, any efficient situation must be one of constant returns for integer changes in scale. The effects of indivisibilities are absent, and there exists a competitive price system for each efficient point such that the efficient point is profit-maximizing.

Suppose all inputs are indivisible and no one of them is assumed to be substitutable for a divisible commodity. Alternatively, suppose all outputs are indivisible and no one of them is assumed to be substitutable for a divisible commodity. The following corollary asserts that if any indivisible commodity is an indirect substitute for all inputs and if there is at least one divisible output, then any efficient point $y^*$ exhibits constant returns and there is a competitive price system such that $y^*$ is profit-maximizing. Alternatively, if any indivisible commodity is an indirect substitute for all outputs and there is at least one divisible input, then there exists a competitive price system for each efficient point $y^*$ such that $y^*$ is profit-maximizing.

COROLLARY 5.3.1a. *Given Postulates A, B, C, D, and E, if for any efficient point $y^*$ each indivisible commodity is an indirect substitute for all inputs (outputs), except perhaps itself, and if at least one output (input) is a divisible commodity, then there exists a competitive price system $p(y) = p > 0$ for all $y$ in $Y$ such that $y^*$ is a profit-maximizing possible point.*

*Proof:* According to Theorem 4.2.2, if any indivisible commodity is an indirect substitute for every input (output), except perhaps itself, then it is an indirect substitute for every output (input), except perhaps itself. Since we assume that at least one output (input) is divisible, the conditions of Theorem 5.3.1 are satisfied.

Another corollary leads directly from the one above.

COROLLARY 5.3.1b. *Given Postulates A, B, C, D, and E, if $n = 2$, if there is one divisible commodity, and if $y^* \neq 0$, then there exists a price vector $p > 0$ such that the possible point $y^*$ is profit maximizing.*

*Proof:* If $y^* \leq 0$, since 0 belongs to $Y$ (Postulate B), $y^*$ is not efficient. If $y^* \geq 0$, then $2 \cdot y^* \geq y^*$, and since $2y^*$ belongs to $Y$ (Postulate A),

$y^*$ is not efficient. By hypothesis we exclude $y^* = 0$. Only two possibilities remain: either (1) $y_1^* < 0$ and $y_2^* > 0$ or (2) $y_1^* > 0$ and $y_2^* < 0$. It follows that for an efficient point $y^*$ there must be one and only one input and one and only one output. If the input (output) is indivisible, it is a substitute for all other indivisible inputs (outputs) since there are no other inputs (outputs). Thus Theorem 5.3.1 always applies.

The reasoning behind Corollary 5.3.1a is similar to the reasoning underlying Theorem 5.3.1. If any unit of an indivisible input is used to less than capacity, efficiency has not been attained. This is because it is possible to substitute this input for all other inputs so that the excess capacity of a unit of this input is reduced by a small amount, and a small amount of excess capacity appears for one unit of each of the other inputs. Since one unit of each and every indivisible input has some excess capacity, it is possible to use these excess capacities to produce more of the divisible output without producing any less of all other outputs. Similarly, if any unit of an indivisible output is only partially completed, then efficiency has not been achieved. It is possible to substitute this output for all indivisible inputs so that the partial completion of that output is reduced by a small amount, and a small amount of excess capacity in a unit of every indivisible input is generated. Then we may increase the output of a divisible commodity by using the excess capacity of all indivisible inputs without using more units of any input and without reducing any other output. Efficiency is only achieved whenever all units of all indivisible inputs are fully employed, and all units of all indivisible outputs are fully completed. Constant returns must always prevail for any efficient point $y^*$ and there always exists a competitive price system such that $y^*$ is a profit-maximizing possible point.

Corollary 5.3.1b asserts that when there are only two commodities and one of them is divisible, constant returns must hold for any efficient point $y^*$, and there is a competitive price system such that $y^*$ is profit-maximizing. This corollary does not generalize to the case of more than two commodities.

In Figure 5.4 the set $Y$ consists of the vertical half lines within the shaded area. The shaded area represents the convex hull of $Y$. There are two commodities. Commodity 1 is indivisible, and commodity 2 is divisible. Any point $y = (y_1\, y_2)$, belonging to $\overline{Y}$, belongs to $Y$ also if and only if $y_1$ is integer. The set $Y$ satisfies the five postulates of additivity, inaction, disposal, closure, and integer convexity. Commodity 1 is an indirect (also a direct) substitute for commodity 2. That is, by increasing the input of commodity 1, we may always increase the output of commodity 2. The indivisible commodity is a substitute for the divisible commodity. Given an efficient point such as $y^*$ in Figure 5.3a, there is a price vector such as $p$ such that $y^*$ is profit-maximizing. The point $y^{**}$ is

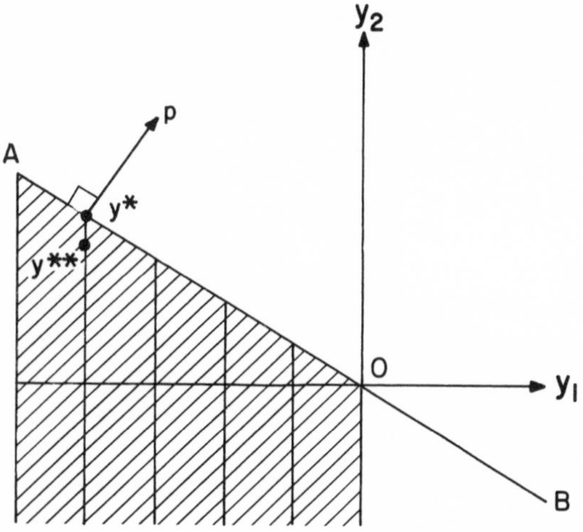


Figure 5.4

not efficient nor is it efficient with respect to $\overline{Y}$. Since $y^{**}$ is not efficient with respect to $\overline{Y}$, a unit of the indivisible input (commodity 1) has excess capacity. It is always possible to achieve greater efficiency. That is, it is always possible to find a point of $Y$ above and to the right of $y^{**}$ which is not efficient with respect to $\overline{Y}$. In Figure 5.3a, the point $y^*$ lies above and to the right of $y^{**}$.

Figure 5.5 shows the attainable set $Z$ derived from the set $Y$ in

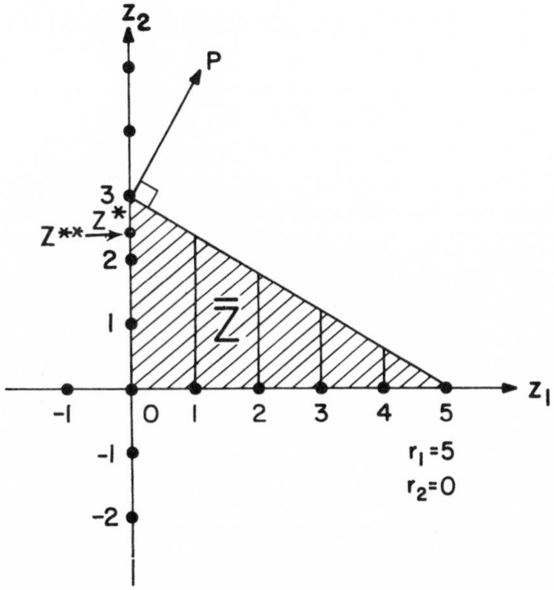


Figure 5.5

Figure 5.4 The set $Z$ consists of the vertical half lines within the shaded area. For any point such as $z^* = r + y^*$ in Figure 5.5, there is always a price vector $p$ such that $z^*$ is a profit-maximizing attainable point because $y^*$ is efficient with respect to $\bar{Y}$. Since $y^{**}$ is not efficient with respect to $\bar{Y}$, there is no assurance that there exists a price vector such that $z^{**} = r + y^{**}$ is profit-maximizing. In fact, as illustrated, there is no price vector such that $z^{**}$ is a profit-maximizing attainable point.

The two-dimensional diagram in Figure 5.4 does not bring out all of the complexities involved, since it is an example of the special case treated in Corollary 5.3b in which there are only two commodities and in which one of them is divisible.

Consider the set $Y$ consisting of all points

$$\begin{pmatrix} y_1 \\ y_2 \\ y_3 \end{pmatrix} = \begin{pmatrix} -3 \\ -2 \\ 2 \end{pmatrix} \cdot \lambda_1 + \begin{pmatrix} -1 \\ -2 \\ 1 \end{pmatrix} \cdot \lambda_2 + \begin{pmatrix} -1 \\ 0 \\ 0 \end{pmatrix} \cdot \lambda_3 + \begin{pmatrix} 0 \\ -1 \\ 0 \end{pmatrix} \cdot \lambda_4 + \begin{pmatrix} 0 \\ 0 \\ -1 \end{pmatrix} \cdot \lambda_5$$

where

$$\lambda_j \geqq 0 \quad \text{for} \quad j = 1, \ldots, 5 \tag{5.3.9}$$

and where

$$y_1 = -3 \cdot \lambda_1 - \lambda_2 - \lambda_3$$

and (5.3.10)

$$y_2 = -2 \cdot \lambda_1 - 2 \cdot \lambda_2 - \lambda_4$$

are integer.

The $\lambda_j$ need not be integer, and the co-ordinate $y_3$ need not be integer. Commodities 1 and 2 are indivisible while commodity 3 is divisible. Figure 5.6 is a projection of this set onto the subspace of indivisible commodities. Projected points of $Y$ are all those points with integer co-ordinates in the non-positive quadrant. These points are shown by heavy dots in Figure 5.6. The figures in parentheses indicate the maximum possible output of commodity 3 for a given combination of commodities 1 and 2 as inputs. Consider the points $(-2, -1)$ and $(-1, -1)$ with the numbers 1 and $\frac{3}{4}$, respectively, in parentheses next to these points in Figure 5.6. These projected points of $Y$ correspond to the possible points $(-2, -1, 1)$ and $(-1, -1, \frac{3}{4})$. One can show that both these points are efficient.

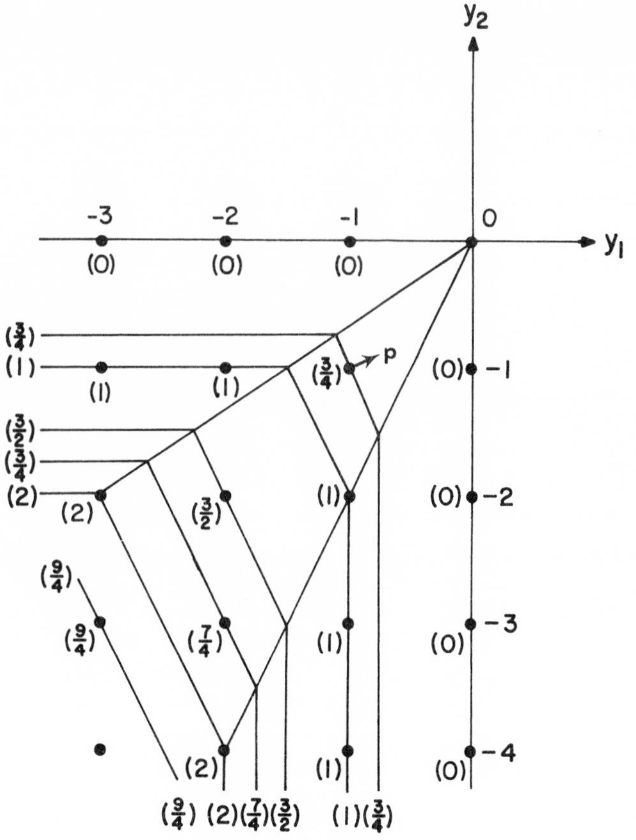


Figure 5.6

Given the point $(-1, -1, \frac{3}{4})$, both of the indivisible commodities 1 and 2 are indirect (also direct) substitutes for the divisible commodity 3. That is, by increasing the input of commodity 1 from 1 to 2 without increasing the input of commodity 2, we may increase the output of the divisible commodity 3, that is, we may go from the point $(-1, -1, \frac{3}{4})$ to the point $(-2, -1, 1)$. Similarly, by increasing the input of commodity 2 from 1 to 2 without increasing the input of commodity 1, we may increase the output of commodity 3, that is, we may go from the point $(-1, -1, \frac{3}{4})$ to the point $(-1, -2, 1)$. Thus for the efficient point $(-1, -1, \frac{3}{4})$, the conditions of Theorem 5.3.1 are satisfied.

In addition, the assumptions of Corollary 5.3.1a are satisfied. The indivisible commodity 1 is an indirect substitute for the only other input, commodity 2, and the indivisible commodity 2 is an indirect substitititute for the only other input, commodity 1. Commodity 2 is an indirect substitute for commodity 1 because if we increase the scale of the point $(-1, -1, \frac{3}{4})$ by a factor of 12, we obtain the possible point $(-12, -12, 9)$, and the possible point $(-9, -18, 9)$ where $(\lambda_1 = 0, \lambda_2 = 9, \lambda_3 = 0, \lambda_4 = 0$, and $\lambda_5 = 0)$ uses less of input 1 and more of input 2 while producing no less of commodity 3 as an output. Similarly, commodity 1 is an indirect substitute for commodity 2 because if we increase the scale of $(-1, -1, \frac{3}{4})$ by 16, we obtain the point $(-16, -16, 12)$, and the possible point $(-18, -12, 12)$ where $(\lambda_1 = 6, \lambda_2 = 0, \lambda_3 = 0, \lambda_4 = 0$, and $\lambda_5 = 0)$ uses less of input 2 and more of input 1 while producing no less of commodity 3 as an output.

Since the assumptions of Theorem 5.3.1 or Corollary 5.3.1a are satisfied and since $\bar{Y}$ is polyhedral in this case, there exists a positive price vector, namely $p = (2, 1, 4)$[2], such that $(-1, -1, \frac{3}{4})$ is a profit-maximizing possible point. Each of the fractured lines which look like isoquants in Figure 5.6 are projections of points in the boundary of $\bar{Y}$, the convex hull of $Y$, which correspond to a given value for $y_3$. The "isoquants" shown in Figure 5.6 correspond to values of $y_3 = \frac{3}{4}, 1, \frac{3}{2}, \frac{7}{4}, 2$, and $\frac{9}{4}$, respectively. These values are noted in parentheses at both ends of each isoquant. The projection of the price vector $p = (2, 1, 4)$ onto the subspace of $y_1$ and $y_2$ is the vector normal to the "isoquant" passing through the point $(-1, -1)$ in Figure 5.6.

Now let us consider the point $(-2, -1)$ in Figure 5.6 which corresponds to the possible point $(-2, -1, 1)$. Given this possible point neither the conditions of Theorem 5.3.1 or Corollary 5.3.1a are satisfied. Commodity 1 is not a substitute for the divisible commodity 3. No matter how much we increase the scale of the point $(-2, -1, 1)$, we cannot increase the input of commodity 1, the input of commodity 2 remaining constant or becoming smaller, so that the output of commodity 3 increases. Thus the conditions of Theorem 5.3.1 are not satisfied. Although, because of the existence of the point $(-1, -2, 1)$, commodity 2 is an indirect substitute for commodity 1, commodity 1 is not an indirect substitute for commodity 2. No matter how much we increase the scale of the point $(-2, -1, 1)$, we cannot increase the input of commodity

[2] The price vector $p = (2, 1, 4)$ was determined by setting $p_2 = 1$ and solving the equations

$$-3 \cdot p_1 - 2 \cdot p_2 + 2 \cdot p_3 = 0$$
$$-1 \cdot p_1 - 2 \cdot p_2 + 1 \cdot p_3 = 0$$

for $p_1$ and $p_3$. From (5.3.8) we see that $p \cdot y$ is given by

$$(2, 1, 4) \cdot \begin{pmatrix} y_2 \\ y_1 \\ y_3 \end{pmatrix} = 0 \cdot \lambda_1 + 0 \cdot \lambda_2 - 2 \cdot \lambda_3 - \lambda_4 - \lambda_5$$

Since from (5.3.9), $y = (y_1, y_2, y_3)$ is only possible if $\lambda_j \geqq 0$ for $j = 1, \ldots, 5$, obviously $p \cdot y \leqq 0$ for all possible $y$ where $p = (2, 1, 4)$. Furthermore $(2, 1, 4) \cdot \begin{pmatrix} -1 \\ -1 \\ \frac{3}{4} \end{pmatrix} = 0$. Thus $(-1, -1, \frac{3}{4})$ is a profit-maximizing possible point.

1 and decrease the input of commodity 2 while producing no less of commodity 3 as an output. Hence the conditions of Corollary 5.3.1a are not satisfied. The only price vectors $p$ which satisfy the condition $p \cdot y \leqq 0$ for all $y$ in $Y$ and $p \cdot (-2, -1, 1) = 0$ are those for which the price of commodity 1 is zero. One example is the price vector $p = (0, 1, 1)$. In other words, the only projected price vectors normal to the isoquant passing through the point $(-2, -1)$ in Figures 5.6 are also normal to the $y_1$ axis.

## 5.4 Near Profit Maximization

In this section we prove two theorems which place an upper limit on the possible loss from an efficient point $y^*$. Remember that $D$ is the set of indices corresponding to the indivisible commodities.

THEOREM 5.4.1. (*near profit maximization*). *Given Postulates A (additivity), B (inaction), C (disposal), D (closure), and E (integer convexity), for each efficient point $y^* \in Y$, there exists a positive price vector $p$ such that $p \cdot y \leqq 0$ for all $y \in Y$ and*

$$-(p \cdot \varepsilon + \sum_{i \in D} p_i) \leqq p \cdot y^* \leqq 0$$

*where $\varepsilon$ is arbitrarily small and positive.*

*Proof:* Let $U$ be the set of points $y \in \bar{Y}$ where $y \geqq y^*$. Let $u = (u_1, u_2, \ldots, u_n)$ where $u_i = 1$ if $i \in D$ and $u_i = 0$ if $i$ does not belong to $D$. We shall demonstrate that $U$ is bounded from above by $y^* + u$. Suppose the contrary, i.e., there exists a $y \in U$ where $y_j > y_j^* + u_j$ for some $i = j$. Then $y = y^* + \alpha$ where $\alpha_i \geqq 0$ for all $i \neq j$ and $\alpha_j > u_j$. Let $w$ be a non-positive vector for which

$$w_i = -\alpha_i$$

$$w_j = \begin{cases} 0 & \text{if } j \notin D \\ -\alpha_j + u_j & \text{if } j \in D. \end{cases} \qquad (5.4.1)$$

According to Theorem 2.9.2, the point $y' = y + w$ belongs to $\bar{Y}$. Since $y = y^* + \alpha$, from (5.4.1), we see that

$$y_i' = y_i^* \qquad \text{for all } i \neq j$$

$$y_i' = \begin{cases} y_j^* + u_j = y_j^* + 1 & \text{if } j \in D \\ y_j^* + \alpha_j & \text{if } j \notin D \end{cases} \qquad (5.4.2)$$

From (5.4.2) we see that the co-ordinates of $y'$ are integer whenever the co-ordinates of $y^*$ are integer. Since $y'$ belongs to $\bar{Y}$, according to Postulate E (integer convexity), the point $y'$ belongs to $Y$. Now $y' \geq y^*$, and hence $y^*$ is not efficient. This is a contradiction.

Obviously the point $y^* + u + \varepsilon$, where $\varepsilon$ is arbitrarily small and positive, is efficient with respect to $\bar{Y}$. We shall demonstrate that it is efficient with respect to $y^* + (A)$ where $(A)$ is the closure of the local possible cone of $y^* + u + \varepsilon$. The local possible cone $A$ is defined as the set of points $t\cdot(y - y^* - u - \varepsilon)$ where $y \in Y$ and $t > 0$. Suppose this were not true. Then there would exist an $a \in (A)$ such that $a \geq 0$. Now since $a$ belongs to the closure of $A$, in any $\varepsilon$-neighborhood of $a$, there must be a point of $A$. That is $a - \varepsilon^* \in A$ for some $\varepsilon^* \neq 0$. Thus $a - \varepsilon^* = t^0[y^0 - (y^* + u + \varepsilon)]$ for some scalar $t^0 > 0$ and $y^0 \in \bar{Y}$. Since $a \geq 0$ and $\varepsilon > 0$, we have

$$(a - \varepsilon^*)\frac{1}{t^0} + \varepsilon = t^0[y^0 - (y^* + u)] \geq 0$$

or

$$y^0 \geq y^* + u$$

for $y^0 \in \bar{Y}$. This contradicts the fact that $U$ is bounded from above by $y^* + u$ so than $y^* + u + \varepsilon$ must be efficient with respect to $y^* + (A)$.

Using the Fundamental Theorem, we have a price vector $p > 0$ such that

$$p\cdot(y^* + u + \varepsilon) \geqq p\cdot y$$

for all $y \in \bar{Y}$. Since $\bar{Y}$ is a convex cone and $\bar{Y}$ contains $Y$

$$0 \geqq p\cdot y^* \geqq p\cdot y - p\cdot(u + \varepsilon)$$

for all $y \in Y$. Since $0 \in \bar{Y}$ (inaction),

$$0 \geqq p\cdot y^* \geqq -p\cdot(u + \varepsilon) = -(p\cdot\varepsilon + \sum_{i\in D} p_i)$$

The reasoning behind Theorem 5.4.1 may be expressed in more concrete terminology. If there are no units of any indivisible inputs which are less than fully utilized and no units of any indivisible output which are less than fully completed, then constant returns prevail, and there always exists a positive price vector such that profits are at a maximum (zero). At the same time the worst that can happen is that a unit of every indivisible input is utilized only slightly, and a unit of every indivisible output is completed nearly fully. The amount of excess capacity of a unit of an indivisible input need never exceed a whole unit's worth since it is always possible to dispose of a unit of an indivisible input which is not being utilized at all. Likewise, the partial completion of a unit of an indivisible output by definition implies that less than a whole unit is completed. Therefore, the most that profits can be less than zero (the greatest possible loss) need never exceed the sum of the prices of all indivisible inputs and outputs.

The near profit maximization theorem (Theorem 5.4.1) was suggested to us by the consideration that with indivisible commodities although not every efficient point lies in the boundary of $\bar{Y}$ (the convex hull of $Y$), we should expect that every efficient point lies at least "relatively close" to the boundary of $\bar{Y}$ and that there is a boundary point of $\bar{Y}$ which lies just above and to the right of an efficient point. The Fundamental Theorem assures us that there is a supporting hyperplane through this boundary point. We should not have "to push" the hyperplane "down too far" in order "to hit" the efficient point, i.e., profits need not be "too" negative. This is illustrated in Figure 5.7. The point $y^*$ is efficient and the point $y^{**}$ is a boundary point of $\bar{Y}$ which lies just above and to the right of $y^*$. The line $AB$ is a hyperplane through $y^{**}$. If we push the hyperplane down just a bit to the line $A'B'$, we hit the efficient point $y^*$. Maximum profits are zero, and the loss of the efficient point $y^*$ is small. The corollary below follows immediately from Theorem 5.4.1.

COROLLARY 5.4.1a. *Given Postulates A, B, C, D, and E, for each efficient attainable point* $z^*$, *there exists a positive price vector* $p$ *such that* $p \cdot z \leqq p \cdot r$ *for all* $z$ *belonging to* $Z$ *and*

$$p \cdot (r - \varepsilon) - \sum_{i \in D} p_i \leqq p \cdot z^* \leqq p \cdot r.$$

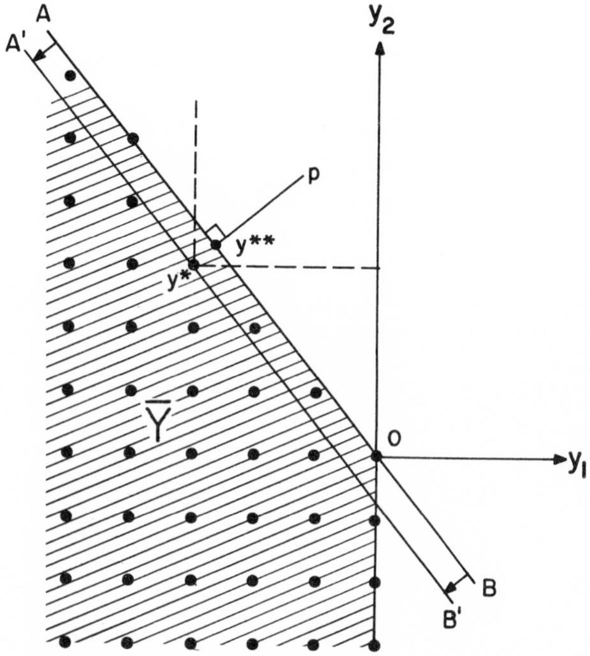


Figure 5.7

*Proof:* According to Theorem 2.5.1, if $z^* = r + y^*$ is efficient, then $y^*$ is efficient. From Theorem 5.4.1 we see that there exists a positive price vector $p$ such that $p \cdot y \leqq 0$ for all $y$ belonging to $Y$. Since $z = r + y$ is an attainable point if and only if $y$ belongs to $Y$, we have $p \cdot z \leqq p \cdot r$. Furthermore, since $-(p \cdot \varepsilon + \sum_{i \in D} p_i) \leqq p \cdot y^* \leqq 0$, we have $p \cdot (r - \varepsilon) - \sum_{i \in D} p_i \leqq pz^* \leqq pr$.

If $p \cdot y^0 = 0$ and $p \cdot y \leqq 0$ for all $y$ belonging to $Y$, then $y^0$ is a profit maximizing possible point. It follows from Theorem 2.12.1 that $z^0 = r + y^0$ is a profit-maximizing attainable point, and maximum profits are $p \cdot z^0 = p \cdot r$. Corollary 5.4.1a says that for every efficient attainable point $z^*$, there exists a positive price vector and a profit maximizing point $z^0$ such that the profit of the point $z^*$, namely $p \cdot z^*$, is never less than maximum profits $p \cdot z^0 = p \cdot r$ by an amount greater than $\sum_{i \in D} p_i + p \cdot \varepsilon$. In particular, if $y^0 = 0$ and $z^0 = r + y^0 = r$, then $p \cdot z^0 = p \cdot r$. The point $z^0$ is a profit-maximizing attainable point and maximum profits are $p \cdot r$. The point $z^*$ is "almost" profit-maximizing. In Figure 5.8, the set $Z$ consists of all the heavy dots within the shaded area. The point $z^0$ is a profit-maximizing attainable point given the price vector $p$. The point $z^*$ is not profit-maximizing, but one need push down the hyperplane just a bit to $A'B'$ to reach the point $z^*$.

Suppose all commodities are indivisible, i.e., the set $D$ contains all $i = 1, \ldots, n$. Then we have the following corollary:

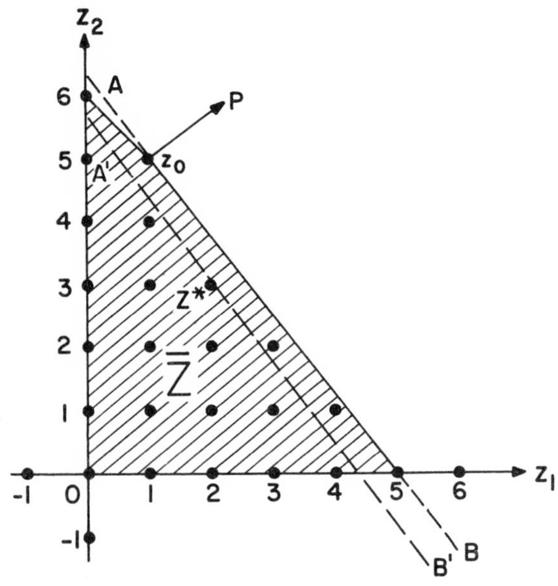


Figure 5.8

COROLLARY 5.4.1b. *Given Postulates A, B, C, D, and E, if* $\bar{Y}$ *is polyhedral and if all commodities are indivisible, for each positive integer* $\lambda$ *and for each efficient point* $y^*$, *there exists a possible point* $y^0$ *and a positive price vector* $p$ *such that* $y^0 \geqq \lambda \cdot y^*$, *and* $p \cdot y^0 > -\sum_{i=1}^n p_i$.

*Proof:* If $y^*$ is efficient with respect to $\bar{Y}$, the theorem is trivial. If $y^*$ is not efficient with respect to $\bar{Y}$, maximize $p^* \cdot y$ over $U$ where $U$ is defined in the proof to Theorem 5.4.1 and $p^* > 0$. We obtain a maximizing point $y^{**} \geq y^*$ which is efficient with respect to $\bar{Y}$. Applying the Fundamental Theorem, there exists a $p > 0$ such that $0 = p \cdot y^{**} \geqq p \cdot y$ for all $y \in \bar{Y}$. Let $\lambda \cdot y^{**} = [\lambda \cdot y^{**}] + f^{**}$, where $[\lambda \cdot y^{**}]$ is an integer vector and where $f^{**}$ is a fractional vector, i.e., $0 \leq f^{**} < (1, \ldots, 1)$. Let $y^0 = [\lambda \cdot y^{**}]$. Now $p \cdot y^0 = p \cdot [\lambda \cdot y^{**}] = p \cdot (\lambda \cdot y^{**} - f^{**}) = -p \cdot f^{**} > -\sum_{i=1}^n p_i$. Also $y^0 = [\lambda \cdot y^{**}] \geqq \lambda \cdot y^*$. Otherwise, there exists an $i = j$ such that $\lambda \cdot y_j^* > [\lambda \cdot y_j^{**}]$ where $[\lambda \cdot y_j^{**}]$ is the $j^{\text{th}}$ co-ordinate of the vector $[\lambda \cdot y^{**}]$. Furthermore, $\lambda \cdot y_j^* - [\lambda \cdot y_j^{**}] \geqq 1$ since $\lambda \cdot y_j^*$ is an integer. This contradicts the inequality $\lambda \cdot y^* \leq \lambda \cdot y^{**} = [\lambda \cdot y^{**}] + f^{**}$ which must hold since $y^{**} \geq y^*$. Thus $y^0 = [\lambda \cdot y^{**}] \geqq \lambda \cdot y^*$.

Corollary 5.4.1b assures us that given an efficient point $y^*$, we may at least double, triple, etc., all outputs with no less (in absolute value terms) than a doubling, tripling, etc., of all inputs and the loss which results is always less than the amount $\sum_{i=1}^n p_i$. The meaning of Corollary 5.4.1b can be made clearer with the use of Figure 5.9. The convex hull of $Y$ is the shaded area, and the set $Y$ consists of all the integer lattice points within the shaded area. All efficient points lie between $A'B'$ and $AB$. The line $AB$ is a supporting hyperplane corresponding to zero (maximum) profits. The line $A'B'$ is a hyperplane corresponding to negative profits, or a loss. Consider the efficient point $(-6, 7)$. If we double the scale of this point we obtain the point $(-12, 14)$. The point $(-12, 14)$ is not efficient. The point $(-11, 14)$ is efficient, however, and represents a doubling of output with less than a doubling of input (in absolute value terms). The point $(-11, 14)$ does not lie very far from the hyperplane of maximum profits $AB$. In fact, it lies between the hyperplane $AB$ and the hyperplane $A'B'$ which represents a small parallel displacement of the line $AB$. Similarly, we can double the scale of the efficient point $(-4, 5)$ and still remain between the two hyperplanes.

Consider any efficient point $y^*$. Let $I_p = \{i | y_i^* > 0\}$. That is, $I_p$ represents the set of indices corresponding to all outputs. We define total revenue from all outputs as $R^* = \sum_{i \in I_p} p_i \cdot y_i^*$. If $p \cdot y^* \leqq 0$, then the ratio $\frac{-p \cdot y^*}{R^*}$ is the loss from the efficient point $y^*$ as a proportion of total revenue. Theorem 5.4.1 asserts that $\frac{-p \cdot y^*}{R^*} \leqq \frac{\sum_{i \in D} p_i + p \cdot \varepsilon}{R^*}$. That is,

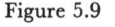

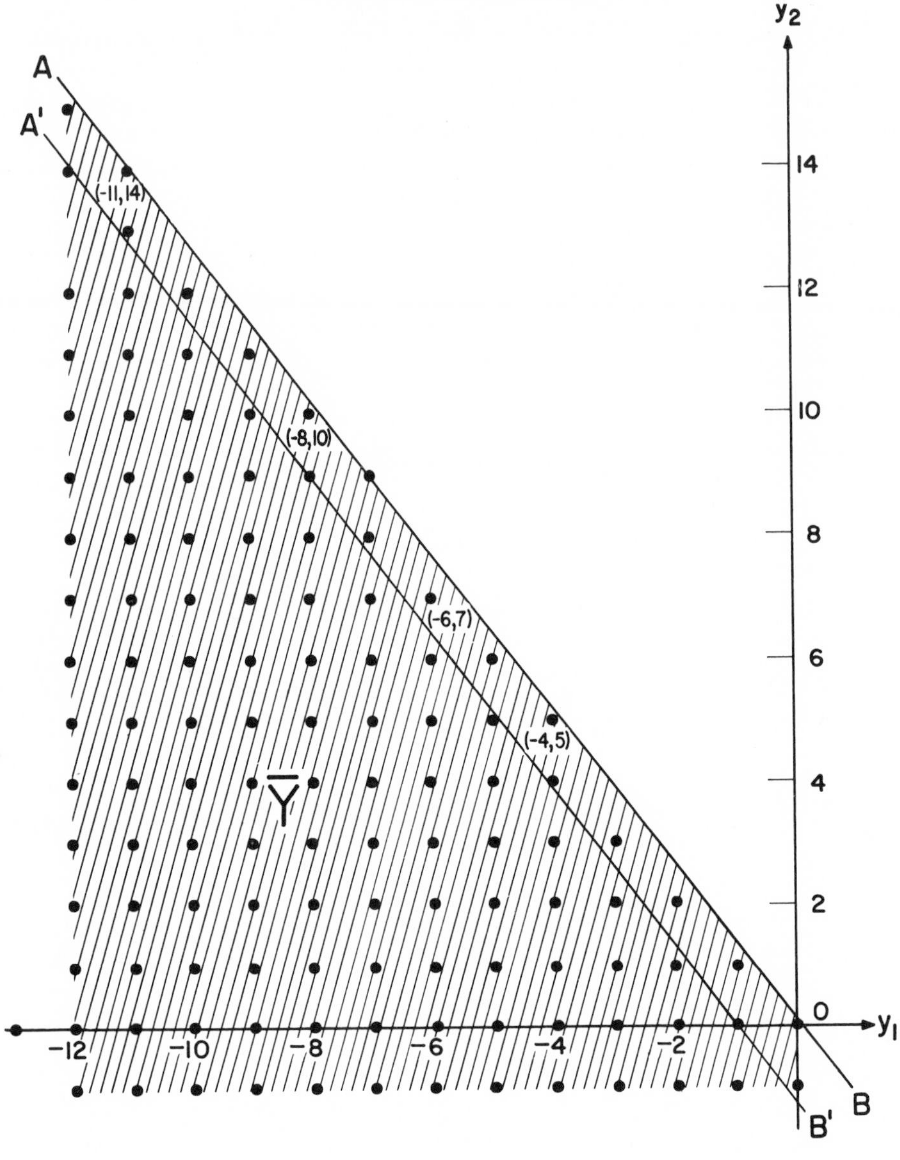


Figure 5.9

losses as a proportion of total revenue never exceeds a certain finite limit. Corollary 5.4.1b further assures us that for each positive integer $\lambda$, there exists a possible point $y^0$ such that $-p \cdot y^0 < \sum_{i \in D} p_i$ and $y^0 \geqq \lambda \cdot y^*$. The revenue of the point $y^0$ is $R^0 = \sum_{i \in I_p} p_i \cdot y_i^0$. Certainly, we have $R^0 \geqq \lambda \cdot R^*$. It is then true that $\frac{-p \cdot y^0}{R^0} \leqq \frac{\sum_{i \in D} p_i}{R^*}$. As $\lambda$ becomes larger and larger, the ratio on the left-hand side of this last inequality becomes smaller and smaller. That is, the loss of the point $y^0$ becomes a smaller and smaller proportion of total revenue. In fact, as $\lambda$ approaches infinity, it is always possible to find a point $y^0 \geqq \lambda \cdot y^*$ such that the loss as a proportion of total revenue approaches zero. Similarly, one may perform the same analysis in terms of the loss to cost ratio, i.e., $\frac{-p \cdot y^*}{C^*}$ where $C = \sum_{i \notin I_p} p_i \cdot y_i^*$. In other words, it is possible to at least double, triple, etc., all outputs with no more than a similar multiplication of inputs (in absolute value terms), and the loss becomes a smaller and smaller proportion of total revenue and a smaller and smaller proportion of total cost. Both the proportions eventually approach zero.

## 5.5 Discriminatory Pricing

Up to this point we have been concerned only with competitive price systems. The price of each commodity is the same regardless of the amount $y_i$ produced as an output or used as an input, i.e., $p(y) = p$ where $p$ is a constant price vector for all $y$ belonging to Y. In this section we shall be concerned with a general class of price systems where the price of each commodity may assume one of two values. In particular, the price of each commodity is given by

$$p_i(y_i) = \begin{cases} p_i & \text{if} \quad y_i > y_i^* \\ p_i + \delta & \text{if} \quad y_i \leqq y_i^* \quad \text{where} \end{cases} \tag{5.5.1}$$

$$p_i(y_i) > 0 \quad \text{for all} \quad i \quad \text{and} \quad \delta \geqq 0.$$

This sort of pricing system is independent (Definition 2.5.1), since the price of one commodity does not depend on the price of another commodity. The pricing system satisfying (5.5.1) is also inverse (Definition 2.10.1) since the price of the $i^{\text{th}}$ commodity does not rise as the amount of the $i^{\text{th}}$ commodity increases. We shall call such a price system a *double price system* to refer to the fact that the price of each commodity may assume one of two different values. If $y_i^*$ is positive, then when the $i^{\text{th}}$ commodity is an input or an output of small magnitude, one price is relevant, but as the output of the $i^{\text{th}}$ commodity exceeds $y_i^*$, the price falls. If $y_i^*$ is negative, then when the $i^{\text{th}}$ commodity is an output or an input of small magnitude (in absolute value terms), one price holds, but as the input of the $i^{\text{th}}$ commodity becomes greater (in absolute value terms) than $|y_i^*|$, then the price rises. If $y_i^* = 0$, then a lower price holds if the $i^{\text{th}}$ commodity is an output than if the $i^{\text{th}}$ commodity is an input.

In this section we deal with discriminatory pricing. The term discriminatory pricing refers to the way in which profit is calculated.

Remember that with discriminatory pricing, profit is calculated as follows:

$$\pi(y) = \sum_{i=1}^{n} \int_{0}^{y_i} p_i(y_i) \cdot dy_i. \qquad (5.5.2)$$

In the last chapter we proved (Theorem 4.4.2) that if there is a price system $p(y)$ for all $y$ belonging to $Y$ such that the point $y^*$ is profit-maximizing with discriminatory pricing, then the point $y^*$ is efficient. Below, we shall prove the converse of this, namely

THEOREM 5.5.1. *Given Postulates A (additivity), B (inaction), C (disposal), D (closure), and E (integer convexity), if all commodities are indivisible ($I = D$), for each efficient point $y^*$, there exists a price system $p(y)$ for all $y$ belonging to $Y$ such that $y^*$ is a profit-maximizing possible point with discriminatory pricing, and $z^* = r + y^*$ is a profiit-maximizing attainable point with discriminatory pricing. In particular, one can determine a price system $p(y)$ which satisfies (5.5.1).*

*Proof:* According to Theorem 5.4.1, there exists a positive price vector $p$ such that

$$-p \cdot \varepsilon - \sum_{i \in D} p_i < p \cdot y^* \leqq 0, \qquad (5.5.3)$$

and

$$p \cdot y \leqq 0 \quad \text{for all} \quad y \in Y. \qquad (5.5.4)$$

Using this positive price vector define a price system $p(y)$ as in (5.5.1) where

$$\delta = -p \cdot y^*. \qquad (5.5.5)$$

Consider any possible point $y'$. Now

$$\pi(y') = \pi(y^*) + \sum_{i=1}^{n} \int_{y_i^*}^{y_i'} p_i(y_i) \cdot dy_i \qquad (5.5.6)$$

Let $I_1 = \{i | y_i' < y_i^*\}$, $I_2 = \{i | y_i' = y_i^*\}$, and $I_3 = \{i | y_i' > y_i^*\}$. Then from (5.5.1) and (5.5.6), we have

$$\pi(y') = \pi(y^*) + \sum_{i=1}^{n} \int_{y_i^*}^{y_i'} p_i \cdot dy_i + \sum_{i \in I_1} \int_{y_i^*}^{y_i'} \delta \cdot dy_i \qquad (5.5.7)$$

Since $p_i$ and $\delta$ are constants, we may write (5.5.7) as

$$\pi(y') = \pi(y^*) + p \cdot (y' - y^*) + \sum_{i \in I_1} \delta \cdot (y_i' - y_i^*) \qquad (5.5.8)$$

From (5.5.5) we see that (5.5.8) becomes

$$\pi(y') = \pi(y^*) + p \cdot y' + \delta + \delta \cdot \sum_{i \in I_1} (y_i' - y_i^*). \qquad (5.5.9)$$

Since $y^*$ is efficient, the set $I_1$ is not empty. As $(y_i' - y_i^*) < 0$ for all $i$ belonging to $I_1$ and as all commodities are indivisible, it follows that

$$\delta \cdot \sum_{i \in I_1} (y_i' - y_i^*) \leqq -\delta. \qquad (5.5.10)$$

From (5.5.4) and (5.5.9), we see that

$$\pi(y') \leqq \pi(y^*) + p \cdot y'. \qquad (5.5.11)$$

Since $p \cdot y' \leqq 0$, we have

$$\pi(y') \leqq \pi(y^*). \qquad (5.5.12)$$

This shows that $y^*$ is a profit-maximizing possible point. It is obvious that this implies also that $z^* = r + y^*$ is a profit-maximizing attainable point.

Let us consider the Figure 5.10. The set $Y$ consists of the heavy dots within the shaded area, and the shaded area is the convex hull $\bar{Y}$. For all points of $Y$ above the horizontal dashed line and to the right of the vertical dashed line (within the area labeled by the Roman numeral I), we have $y_1 > y_1^*$ and $y_2 > y_2^*$. Hence within the area labeled I, the prices $p_1(y_1) = p_1$ and $p_2(y_2) = p_2$ are relevant. For all points above the horizontal dashed line and to the left of the vertical dashed line (within the area labeled II), we have $y_1 < y_1^*$ and $y_2 > y_2^*$. Thus within the area labeled II the prices $p_1(y_1) = p_1 + \delta$ and $p_2(y_2) = p_2$ are relevant.

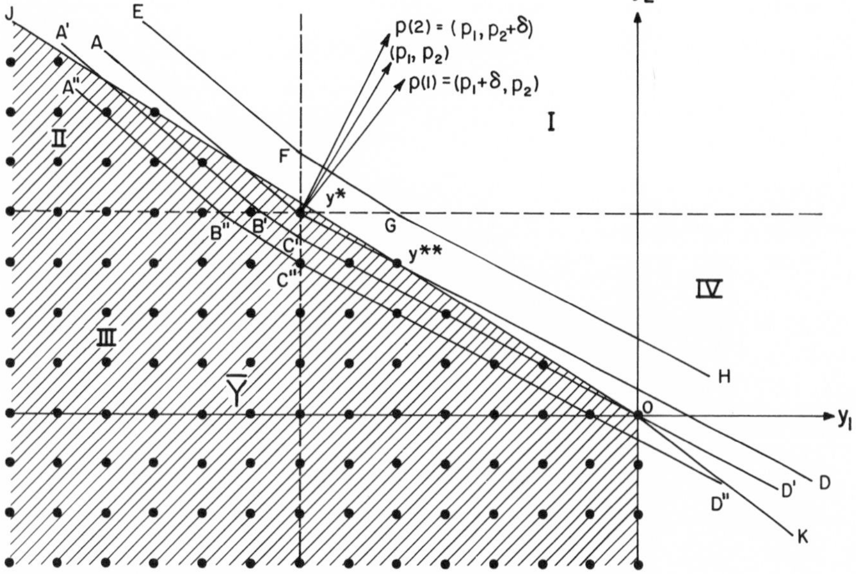


Figure 5.10

Similarly, within the area labeled III, the prices $p_1(y_1) = p_1 + \delta$ and $p_2(y_2) = p_2 + \delta$ hold. Finally, within the area labeled IV, we have the prices $p_1(y_1) = p_1$ and $p_2(y_2) = p_2 + \delta$. The broken line segment $A''B''C''D''$ is an iso-profit line in the sense that all possible points lying on this line give equal profits with discriminatory pricing. All points on $A''B''C''D''$ give rise to negative profits (losses). The broken line segment $A'B'C'D'$ is an iso-profit line corresponding to zero profits. The iso-profit line $Ay^*D$ corresponds to positive profits. The point $y^*$ is profit maximizing, and $y^*$ is efficient. If $y^*$ were not efficient, then there would be a possible point which would correspond to higher profits, e.g., profits corresponding to the iso-profit line *EFGH*. The point $y^{**}$ in Figure 5.10 is also profit-maximizing with discriminatory pricing, and $y^{**}$ is efficient.

Theorem 5.5.1 was suggested to us by the consideration that an efficient point lies "relatively close" to the boundary of $\bar{Y}$ although it may not lie in the boundary itself. As was shown in Theorem 5.4.1, there exists a supporting hyperplane through some point of $\bar{Y}$ above and to the right of $y^*$. It should be possible to "bend" or "indent" the hyperplane so that it becomes a cone with $y^*$ at its vertex. The line $JK$ in Figure 5.10 is a supporting hyperplane. We can bend the hyperplane $JK$ by rotating the price vector $p$ which is normal to $JK$ in one direction to $p(1)$ and then rotating $p$ in the other direction to $p(2)$. The rotation to $p(1)$ is performed by increasing the price on commodity 1. The rotation to $p(2)$ is performed by increasing the price on commodity 2. In $n$-dimensions the normal vector $p$ is rotated in $n$ different directions by increasing the price of each commodity successively. The $n$ different price vectors $p(j)$ for $j = 1, \ldots, n$ determined in this fashion have co-ordinates

$$p_i(j) = \begin{cases} p_i & \text{if} \quad i \neq j \quad \text{where} \quad \delta > 0 \\ p_j + \delta & \text{if} \quad i = j. \end{cases} \tag{5.5.13}$$

Using these $n$ price vectors, we may generate a cone which is the intersection of the $n$ half-spaces

$$p(j) \cdot y \geqq p(j) \cdot y^* \quad \text{for} \quad j = 1, \ldots, n. \tag{5.5.14}$$

This cone has the following properties: (*a*) Its vertex is $y^*$. (*b*) No point in the interior of the cone is a point of $Y$. (*c*) The boundary of the cone is an iso-profit surface with discriminatory pricing where the pricing system $p(y)$ satisfies (5.5.1). That is, each point $y$ in the boundary of the cone gives equal profits $\pi(y)$. (*d*) Any point in the interior of the cone gives rise to higher profits and any point outside the cone gives rise to lower profits than a point in the boundary of the cone.

One might call this cone a supporting cone through $y^*$. Theorem 5.5.1 establishes the existence of a supporting cone for each efficient point $y^*$.

In Figure 5.10 the supporting cone is represented by the area which lies above and to the right of $Ay^*D$. The boundary of this cone, namely the broken line segment $Ay^*D$, is an iso-profit surface in that any point which lies on $Ay^*D$ gives equal profit. No point in the interior of this cone is a point of $Y$, and all points in the interior give a higher profit than any point on the boundary. All points outside the cone give a lower profit.

In Figure 5.11 the attainable set $Z$ consists of the heavy dots within the shaded areas. The shaded area represents the convex hull of $Z$. The point $z^*$ is an efficient attainable point. Here the broken line segment $Az^*D$ is an iso-profit line with discriminatory pricing and a price system $p(y)$ which satisfies (5.5.1). Any point within the supporting cone (above and to the right of $Az^*D$) gives rise to a higher profit and any point in $Z$ is outside the supporting cone and gives rise to a lower profit than the point $z^*$. The point $z^*$ is a profit-maximizing attainable point. In fact according to Theorem 5.5.1, for any efficient attainable point $z^*$, one may always find a double price system such that $z^*$ is profit-maximizing with discriminatory pricing. That is, one may always find a supporting cone through the efficient attainable point $z^*$.

What is the economic rationale behind discriminatory pricing? As we have shown before, there may be efficient input-output combinations

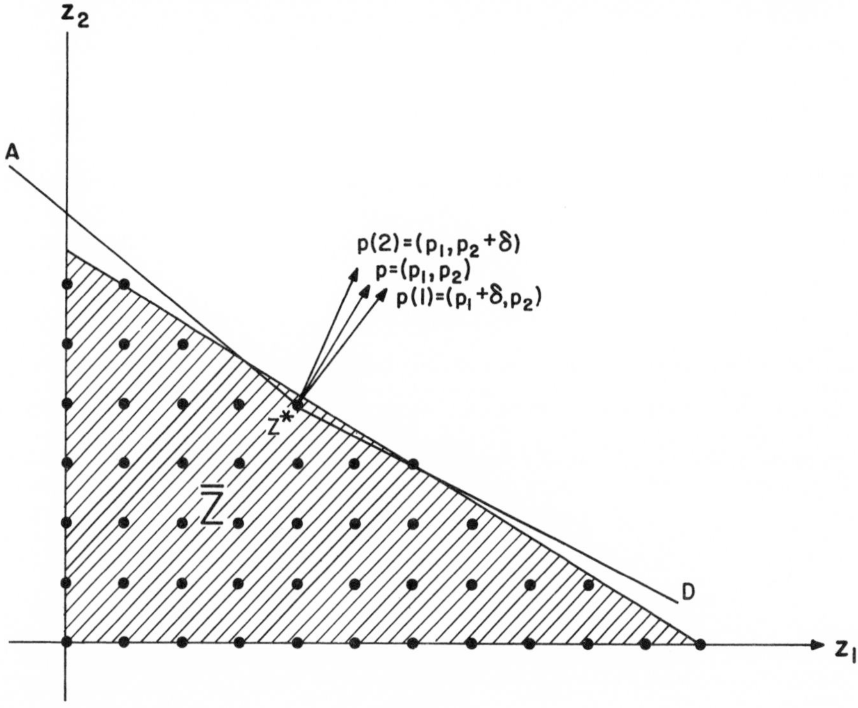


Figure 5.11

which are not profit-maximizing with any conceivable competitive price system. When this is the case, there are increasing returns for integer changes in scale. If, however, the price of an indivisible output is high for the first units produced and lower for later units, and if the price of an indivisible input is low for the first units used and higher for later units, then such an efficient input-output combination is profit-maximizing with discriminatory pricing. The higher price for earlier units of output and the lower price for later units of output help compensate for the loss which would be incurred if a competitive price system $p(y) = p$ were being used. The lower price for later units of output and the higher price for later units of input prevent the profit maximizer from taking advantage of increasing returns through an integer increase in scale.

## 5.6 Conclusions

Substitution between indivisible commodities and divisible commodities leads to constant returns. Thus substitution implies the efficacy of competitive pricing mechanisms. Several authors have hinted at this possibility. For example, Stigler maintains that in order to eliminate the effects of indivisibility "one may use trucks instead of railroads, ferries or detours instead of bridges, etc."[3]

For those efficient input-output combinations which exhibit increasing returns, however, there is no choice except to abandon the competitive pricing mechanism as a way of achieving efficiency. Theorem 5.4.1 suggests that some finite subsidy is necessary to induce an economic agent to operate under increasing returns. The idea that a bounty or subsidy may be necessary to induce an industry or a firm to produce at a point of increasing returns is an old one and has been proposed by Marshall,[4] Pigou,[5] Lerner,[6] and Kahn[7] among others. As Kemp[8] has

[3] G. Stigler, *Theory of Price* (New York: Macmillan, 1952), p. 138.

[4] Alfred E. Marshall, *Principles of Economics* (8th ed., London: Macmillan, 1932), Book V, Chapter XIII.

[5] A. C. Pigou states: "It follows that, under conditions of simple competition, for every industry in which the value of the marginal social net product is greater than that of the marginal private net product, there will be certain rates of bounty, the granting of which by the state would modify output is such a way as to make the value of the marginal social net product more nearly equal to the marginal social net product of resources in general, thus—provided that the funds for the bounty can be raised by a mere transfer that does not inflict direct injury on production—increasing the size of the national dividend and the sum of economic welfare." *The Economics of Welfare* (4th ed., London: Macmillan, 1938), p. 224.

[6] A. P. Lerner, *The Economics of Control* (New York: Macmillan, 1944), p. 177.

[7] R. F. Kahn writes: "If economies are the exception and not the rule, so that it is the outputs of only a small number of industries which have to be interferred with in order to bring them up to the ideal level, a scheme of bounties obviously offers the simplest method of bringing about the required diversion of resources, . . ." from "Some Notes on Ideal Output," *The Economic Journal*, Vol. 45 (March 1935), p. 11.

[8] Murray Kemp, "The Efficiency of Competition as an Allocator of Resources," *Canadian Journal of Economics and Political Science*, Vol. 21 (Feb. 1955), p. 30.

pointed out, however, one must be careful in interpreting this notion of a bounty as a method of achieving efficiency. A given subsidy is only valid for a particular input-output combination. If the subsidy is specified to be paid for all outputs, then it will still pay a firm either to expand or to shut down if it is operating at a point of increasing returns.

Theorem 5.4.1 and Corollary 5.4.1b suggest another alternative to a competitive pricing and profit-maximizing mechanism for achieving efficiency. We may forsake any behavioral assumption of profit maximization as the motive of an economic agent and substitute the assumption that his motive is to achieve a level of profits which are "sufficiently close" to the maximum level of profit.[9]

As another alternative to perfectly competitive pricing and profit maximization, Theorem 5.5.1 suggests a special type of discriminatory pricing. The discriminatory prices which perform this task are of a particularly simple sort. Two prices are specified for each commodity. One price holds below a certain amount and the other price holds above that amount. The notion that indivisibilities imply that production decisions should be based on discriminatory pricing is an old one, expounded as early as 1844 by Dupuit.[10] Such arguments for discrimination are usually based on the notion of consumer surplus,[11] or on some variation of the notion that the fixed costs of firms which operate under conditions of increasing returns must be covered by resort to discrimination.[12] In our analysis we have all but neglected the consumer side of the picture, and we have not found it necessary to enter upon any discussion of fixed costs. In mathematical terms the argument rests on the fact that with indivisibilities certain efficient points do not lie on the boundary of the convex hull of the set of production possibilities, and it is not possible to find a supporting hyperplane for such efficient points although it is possible to find a supporting cone, the surface of which is an iso-profit surface with

[9] This is the hypothesis which is used in the theory of heuristic programming. One may reason that in most real life instances, it is either impossible or extremely costly for any individual or group of individuals to assess all alternative possible actions in order to select one which leads to an optimal solution. Rather one seeks a "satisficing" solution which comes close to a maximum and can be achieved by a less complicated set of decision rules or in a less costly manner. See Robert Ferber and P. J. Verdoorn, *Research Methods in Economics and Business* (New York: Macmillan, 1962), pp. 199–201. See also Fred Tonge, *A Heuristic Program for Assembly Line Balancing* (New York: Prentice-Hall, 1961) and Herbert A. Simon, "Theories of Decision Making in Economics," *American Economic Review*, Volume XLIX (June 1959), pp. 262–264.

[10] Jules Dupuit, "De la Mésure de l'Utilité des Travaux Publiques," *Annales des Ponts et Chausées*, 2nd series, Vol. 8 (1844), reprinted in *International Economic Papers*, No. 2 (1952), pp. 83–110.

[11] See Abba P. Lerner, *The Economics of Control*, pp. 190–198, A. C. Pigou, *The Economics of Welfare*, Part II, Chapter XVII, and J. R. Hicks, "The Rehabilitation of Consumers' Surplus," *Review of Economic Studies*, Vol. VIII (Feb. 1941), 108–116.

[12] A. M. Henderson, "The Pricing of Public Utility Undertakings," *The Manchester School* (September 1947), p. 242 and J. M. Clark, *Studies in the Economics of Overhead Costs*, (Chicago: Chicago University Press, 1923), Chapter XX.

discriminatory pricing. Another way of stating it is that in order for a firm to be induced to produce at a point of increasing returns, a higher price must be charged for the first units of output than the price charged for later units of output, and a lower price must be charged for the first units of input than for later units. Otherwise, if the prices for all units were the same, either it would pay the firm to expand (if the prices of outputs were high enough and the prices of inputs low enough) or it would pay to shut down (if prices were such that a loss was being made).

Another way of viewing the pricing system proposed in Theorem 5.5.1 is in terms of a system of taxes or subsidies for each commodity. Purchases of any commodity may be subsidized up to a certain amount and taxed for purchases exceeding that amount.

# CHAPTER 6

## *INTEGER ACTIVITY ANALYSIS*

In this chapter a production technology is defined in terms of a finite set of possible input-output combinations called *activities*. Integer linear combinations of these activities also produce possible input-output combinations. This chapter includes an analysis of various pricing and profit maximization theorems analogous to those derived for the more general technology in Chapters 2 through 5.

### 6.1 The Technology

The set $Y$ of production possibilities is built up by assuming that there exists a finite number $m$ of activities. The $j^{\text{th}}$ activity is a vector $A_j = (a_{1j}, a_{2j}, \ldots, a_{nj})$ of $n$-dimensions. We assume that $A_j$ is an integer vector and that the point $y = -A_j$ is a possible point, i.e., $y = -A_j \in Y$ for $j = 1, 2, \ldots, m$. Thus, if $-a_{ij} \geqq 0$, then the $i^{\text{th}}$ commodity is an output. If $-a_{ij} \leqq 0$, then the $i^{\text{th}}$ commodity is an input. We assume inaction and additivity so that the vector $y = -A_j \cdot x_j$ is also a possible point where $x_j$ is a *non-negative*, *integer* scalar called the *activity level* of the $j^{\text{th}}$ activity. Furthermore

$$y = -\sum_{j=1}^{m} A_j \cdot x_j \tag{6.1.1}$$

is a possible point where all $x_j$ are non-negative, integer scalars. We write

$$x_j \geqq 0, \quad \text{and} \quad x_j \equiv 0 \pmod 1 \quad \text{for} \quad j = 1, \ldots, m \tag{6.1.2}$$

where $x_j \equiv 0 \pmod 1$ means $x_j$ is a multiple of 1, i.e., an integer, and is read $x_j$ is equivalent to 0 modulo 1.

The points $y$ which satisfy (6.1.1) and (6.1.2) form the totality of all possible points, the set $Y$. It is easy to show that the convex hull $\bar{Y}$ of $Y$ is the set of points $y$ which satisfy (6.1.1) and

$$x_j \geqq 0 \quad \text{for} \quad j = 1, \ldots, n. \tag{6.1.3}$$

The convex hull $\bar{Y}$ is a convex polyhedral cone.

Let $r$ be a resource vector. Then

$$z = y + r \geqq 0 \tag{6.1.4}$$

is an attainable point if $y$ satisfies (6.1.1) and (6.1.2). Let $p$ be a positive price vector. Then

$$\pi = p \cdot z = p \cdot y + p \cdot r \tag{6.1.5}$$

is the profit of the attainable point $z$. A profit-maximizing attainable point $z^* = y^* + r$ maximizes (6.1.5) subject to (6.1.1), (6.1.2) and (6.1.4). The point $y^*$ *is* an efficient possible point. The question to which we will address ourselves in this chapter is what kinds of pricing mechanisms will make $y^*$ a profit-maximizing possible point.

Let us first consider one special case. Let us neglect the integer restrictions on the activity levels $x_j$. Then let $z^* = r + y^*$ maximize (6.1.5) subject to (6.1.1), (6.1.3), and (6.1.4). The point $y^*$ then belongs to the convex hull $\bar{Y}$ and is efficient with respect to $\bar{Y}$. If $y^* = -\sum_{j=1}^{m}, A_j \cdot x_j^*$ and the $x_j^*$ are in fact integer, then $y^*$ is an efficient possible point. Under these conditions, a positive price vector $p^*$ exists such that $p^* \cdot y^* \geqq p \cdot y$ for all $y \in Y$, i.e., satisfies (6.1.1) and (6.1.2). The price vector $p^*$ is related to the price vector $p$ and the "dual" or "shadow" prices of a linear programming problem which we shall demonstrate.[1]

## 6.2 The Linear Programming Case

Let us show how one finds a point $z^* = y^* + r$ which maximizes (6.1.5) subject to (6.1.1), (6.1.3), and (6.1.4) (ignoring the integer restrictions on the $x_j$). Substitute the value of $y$ given in (6.1.1) into (6.1.4) and (6.1.5). The profit-maximizing point $z^*$ maximizes

$$\pi = -\sum_{j=1}^{m} p \cdot (A_j \cdot x_j) + p \cdot r \tag{6.2.1}$$

subject to

$$z + \sum_{j=1}^{m} A_j \cdot x_j = r; \tag{6.2.2}$$

and

$$z \geqq 0 \quad \text{and} \quad x_j \geqq 0 \quad \text{for} \quad j = 1, 2, \ldots, m. \tag{6.2.3}$$

We may modify (6.2.1) by assuming that $\pi_j = -p \cdot A_j$ for $j = 1, \ldots, m$ and $p \cdot r = \pi_0$. Thus we maximize

$$\pi = \pi_0 + \sum_{j=1}^{m} \pi_j \cdot x_j \tag{6.2.4}$$

subject to (6.2.2) and (6.2.3). This is a standard linear programming (LP) format. There are $m + n$ ($z$ and $x_j$) variables. The $z$ variables in standard linear programming terminology may be called slack variables.

The revised simplex method of solving this problem works on the premise that the $m + n$ variables may be divided arbitrarily into two groups, one containing $n$ variables $w$ called the basic variables and one

[1] Throughout this chapter it will be useful for the reader to have some familiarity with linear programming, the dual prices in a linear program, and the revised simplex method of solving linear programming problems. See W. J. Baumol, *Economic Theory and Operations Analysis*, 2nd edn. (Englewood Cliffs, New Jersey: Prentice-Hall, 1965), pp. 70–128.

containing $m$ variables $v$ called the non-basic variables. Then (6.2.4), (6.2.2) and (6.2.3) can be written

$$\pi = \pi_0 + \sum_{i=1}^{n} b_i \cdot w_i + \sum_{j=1}^{m} n_j \cdot v_j; \tag{6.2.5}$$

$$\sum_{i=1}^{n} B_i \cdot w_i + \sum_{j=1}^{m} N_j \cdot v_j = r; \tag{6.2.6}$$

$$\begin{aligned} w_i &\geqq 0 \quad \text{for} \quad i = 1, \ldots, n, \quad \text{and} \\ v_j &\geqq 0 \quad \text{for} \quad j = 1, \ldots, m. \end{aligned} \tag{6.2.7}$$

The vectors $B_i$ are assumed to be linearly independent.[2] They form the columns of a matrix $B$ called the basis matrix or sometimes just the basis.

We may solve (6.2.6) for the basic variables $w_i$ in terms of the non-basic variables $v_j$ and substitute these values into (6.2.5). The result is

$$w_i = \sum_{k=1}^{n} b_{ik}^{-1} \cdot r_k - \sum_{j=1}^{m} \left( \sum_{k=1}^{n} b_{ik}^{-1} \cdot n_{kj} \right) \cdot v_j \quad \text{for} \quad i = 1, 2, \ldots, n, \tag{6.2.8}$$

and

$$\pi = \pi_0 + \sum_{k=1}^{n} \left( \sum_{i=1}^{n} b_i \cdot b_{ik}^{-1} \right) \cdot r_k + \sum_{j=1}^{m} \left[ n_j - \sum_{k=1}^{n} \left( \sum_{i=1}^{n} b_i \cdot b_{ik}^{-1} \right) \cdot n_{kj} \right] \cdot v_j, \tag{6.2.9}$$

where $b_{ik}^{-1}$ is the element in the $i^{\text{th}}$ row and $k^{\text{th}}$ column of the inverse matrix of $B$, $r_k$ is the $k^{\text{th}}$ element of the vector $r$, and $n_{kj}$ is the $k^{\text{th}}$ element of the vector $N_j$.

Corresponding to any basis $B$ is a set of $n$ dual prices, one for each commodity. The dual prices may be defined in a number of different but equivalent ways. The one which we choose is:

$$p_k^0 = \sum_{i=1}^{n} b_i \cdot b_{ik}^{-1} \quad \text{for} \quad k = 1, 2, \ldots, n \tag{6.2.10}$$

where $p_k^0$ is the $k^{\text{th}}$ dual price. Thus we may rewrite (6.2.9) as follows:

$$\pi = \pi_0 + \sum_{k=1}^{n} p_k^0 \cdot r_k + \sum_{j=1}^{m} \left( n_j - \sum_{k=1}^{n} p_k^0 \cdot n_{kj} \right) \cdot v_j. \tag{6.2.11}$$

[2] By linearly independent we mean that $\sum_{i=1}^{n} B_i \cdot x_i = 0$ if and only if all the scalars $x_i = 0$ for $i = 1, \ldots, n$.

A basis $B$ is said to be optimal if

$$\sum_{k=1}^{n} b_{ik}^{-1} \cdot r_k \geqq 0 \quad \text{for} \quad i = 1, \ldots, n \tag{6.2.12}$$

and

$$\pi_j^0 = n_j - \sum_{k=1}^{n} p_k^0 \cdot n_{kj} \leqq 0 \quad \text{for} \quad j = 1, \ldots, m. \tag{6.2.13}$$

If the basis $B$ is optimal, then an optimal solution to the linear programming problem is

$$\begin{aligned} w_i^* &= \sum_{k=1}^{n} b_{ik}^{-1} \cdot r_k \quad \text{for} \quad i = 1, \ldots, n, \quad \text{and} \\ v_j^* &= 0 \qquad\qquad\quad \text{for} \quad j = 1, \ldots, m. \end{aligned} \tag{6.2.14}$$

This optimal solution in terms of the basic and non-basic variables corresponds to a set of optimal values $z^*$ and $x_j^*$ for the $z$ and $x_j$ variables depending on how the partioning of these variables into basic and non-basic variables was made. An optimal value $y^*$ of the $y$ vector is also implied through (6.1.1).

The dual prices $p_k^0$ associated with the *optimal* basis have the following properties:

PI. Consider the possible point $y = -A_j$. The profitability $p^* \cdot y$ of such a point is less than or equal to zero given the price vector $p^* = p + p^0$ where $p^0 = (p_1^0, p_2^0, \ldots, p_n^0)$ is the vector of dual prices. If $x_j$ is a basic variable then $p^* \cdot (-A_j) = 0$.

*Proof:* Let us rewrite (6.2.13) in terms of the $z$ and $x$ variables. If $v_j$ is a $z$ variable, then $n_j = 0$ and $n_{kj} = 0$ for $j \neq k$ with $n_{kj} = 1$ for $j = k$. Thus

$$\pi_j^0 = -p_j^0 \leqq 0 \quad \text{if} \quad v_j = z_j. \tag{6.2.15}$$

If $v_j$ is an $x_j$ variable, then $n_j = -p \cdot A_j$ and $n_{kj} = a_{ij}$ which is the $i$ element of the vector $A_j$. Thus from (6.2.13)

$$\pi_j^0 = -p \cdot A_j - p^0 \cdot A_j = -(p + p^0) \cdot A_j \leqq 0 \quad \text{if} \quad v_j = x_j. \tag{6.2.16}$$

Now if $x_i$ is a basic $w_i$ variable, then

$$\begin{aligned} (p^0 + p)(-A_i) &= -p \cdot A_i - p^0 \cdot A_i \\ &= b_i - \sum_{i=1}^{n} p_k^0 \cdot b_{ki}, \end{aligned} \tag{6.2.17}$$

or from (6.2.10)

$$\begin{aligned} (p^0 + p)(-A_i) &= b_i - \sum_{k=1}^{n} \left( \sum_{i=1}^{n} b_i \cdot b_{ik}^{-1} \right) \cdot b_{ki} \\ &= b_i - b_i = 0. \end{aligned} \tag{6.2.18}$$

The expressions (6.2.16) and (6.2.18) validate the assertion PI.

PII. The dual prices $p_k^0$ are non-negative. If $z_k$ is basic, then $p_k^0 = 0$.
*Proof:* Suppose $z_k$ is basic. Then since $b_{ki} = 1$ for $i = k$ and $b_{ki} = 0$ for $i \neq k$, it follows from (6.2.10) that

$$p_k^0 = \sum_{k=1}^{n} \left( \sum_{i=1}^{n} b_i \cdot b_{ik}^{-1} \right) \cdot b_{ki} = b_k = 0. \qquad (6.2.19)$$

From (6.2.15) we see that $p_j \geqq 0$ for $z_j$ non-basic. Thus assertion PII is proved.

PIII. If $z_k^* > 0$, then $p_k^0 = 0$ and if $p_k^0 > 0$, then $z_k^* = 0$. In economic terminology, if a resource is less than fully utilized, its price is 0. If a positive price is given to a resource it is fully utilized.
*Proof:* This assertion follows immediately from PI and PII since from (6.2.14) the only positive $z_k^*$ are basic variables.

PIV. The price vector $p^* = p + p^0$ is positive and $p^* \cdot y^* = 0 \geqq p \cdot y$ for all $y \in \overline{Y}$, i.e., $y$ which satisfy (6.1.1) and (6.1.3).
*Proof:* From PI

$$(p^0 + p) \cdot y = (p^0 + p)\left( - \sum_{j=1}^{m} A_j \cdot x_j \right) \leqq 0. \qquad (6.2.20)$$

On the other hand if $x_j$ is basic then from PI, $-(p^0 + p) \cdot A_j \cdot x_j^* = 0$ and if $x_j$ is non-basic $-(p^0 + p) \cdot A_j \cdot x_j^* = 0$ since $x_j^* = 0$. Thus

$$(p^0 + p) \cdot y^* = (p^0 + p)\left( - \sum_{j=1}^{m} A_j \cdot x_j^* \right) = 0. \qquad (6.2.21)$$

PV. The optimal profit level $\pi^*$ is equal to the resources valued at prices $p^* = p^0 + p$, i.e., $\pi^* = p^* \cdot r$.
*Proof:* From (6.2.11) and given $\pi_0 = p \cdot r$ and $v_j^* = 0$ for $j = 1, 2, \ldots, m$, it follows that

$$\pi^* = p \cdot r + p^0 \cdot r = (p + p^0) \cdot r = p^* \cdot r. \qquad (6.2.22)$$

PVI. The profit maximum $\pi^* = p \cdot z^*$ can be regarded as a function of $r$, the resource vector. Suppose we change $r$ by an amount $\Delta r$ in such a way that the basis $B$ remains optimal. Then $\pi^*(r + \Delta r) = \pi^*(r) + p^* \cdot \Delta r$. If one resource $r_i$ is changed by an amount $\Delta r_i$, then $\pi^*(r + \Delta r) = \pi^*(r) + p_i^* \cdot \Delta r_i$ and $p_i^*$ is called the *marginal profitability* of the $i^{\text{th}}$ resource.
*Proof:* Whenever $B$ remains an optimal basis, the dual prices $p^0$ remain the same and from PV,

$$\pi^*(r) = p^* \cdot r \quad \text{and}$$
$$\pi^*(r + \Delta r) = p^*(r + \Delta r) \quad \text{or} \qquad (6.2.23)$$
$$\pi^*(r + \Delta r) = \pi^*(r) + p^* \cdot \Delta r. \qquad (6.2.24)$$

If $y^* = -\sum_{j=1}^{m} A_j \cdot x_j^*$ where the $x_j^*$ are integer, then $z^* = r + y^*$ can be regarded as a profit-maximizing attainable point and all propositions PI through PV can be regarded as statements which refer to a profit-maximizing attainable point $z^*$ and a profit-maximizing possible point $y^*$. In particular, PIV can be reformulated to read

> PIV*. If $y^* = -\sum_{j=1}^{m} A_j \cdot x_j^*$ and $x_j^*$ is integer for all $j$, then there exists a positive price vector $p^* = p + p^0$ such that $y^*$ is a profit-maximizing possible point.

Whenever the $x_j^*$ are not integer, however, propositions PIII through PVI must be modified substantially. Propositions PI and PII are generally valid for any basis $B$ which is LP optimal for some $r$.

## 6.3 A Digression into Some Number Theory

Let $B$ be any $n$ by $n$ matrix whose columns $B_i$ are linearly independent. Then given two vectors $q$ and $s$, we write

$$q \equiv s \pmod{B} \tag{6.3.1}$$

if and only if

$$q - s = \sum_{i=1}^{n} B_i \cdot t_i \quad \text{with} \quad t_i \text{ integer} \quad \text{for} \quad i = 1, \ldots, n. \tag{6.3.2}$$

In other words, $q$ and $s$ differ by some integer linear combination of the columns of $B$.

Geometrically, the equivalence relationship (6.3.1) is illustrated by Figure 6.1. The columns of the basis $B$ are represented by points $B_1$ and $B_2$ in two-dimensional space. Integer linear combinations of $B_1$ and $B_2$ are represented by the corners of the set of solid parallelograms (parallelepipeds in three-dimensional space). We note that in Figure 6.1 $r \equiv r'$ (mod $B$). The corners of the parallelograms are all translated by the vector $r$ to form a set of dashed parallelograms. Both $r$ and $r'$ are corner points of the translated parallelograms so that they differ by an integer linear combination of $B_1$ and $B_2$.

The set of points

$$q = \sum_{i=1}^{n} B_i \cdot t_i \quad \text{for} \quad t_i \text{ integer} \tag{6.3.3}$$

forms a lattice of points in $n$-dimensional space (the corners of the parallelograms in Figure 6.1). The lattice generated by $B$ is called the $B$ lattice. The set of points

$$q = \sum_{i=1}^{n} B_i \cdot \lambda_i, \qquad 0 \leqq \lambda_i < 1 \quad \text{for} \quad i = 1, \ldots, n \tag{6.3.4}$$

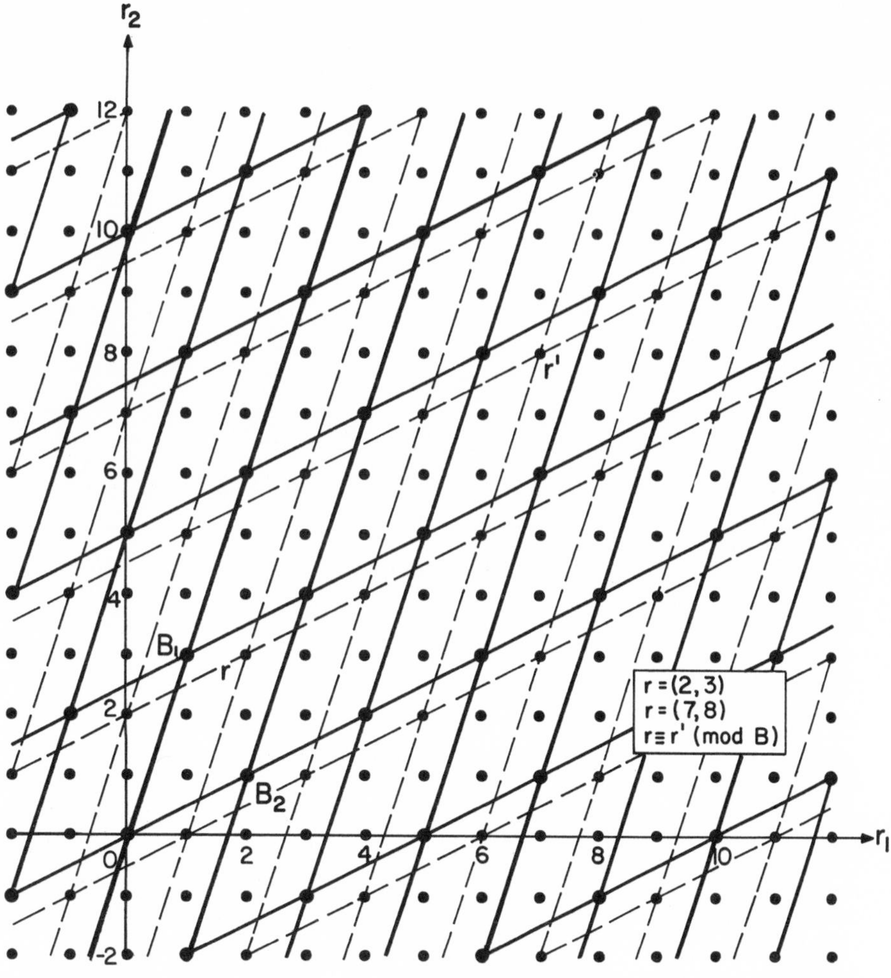


Figure 6.1

is called the fundamental parallelogram of the $B$ lattice. In Figure 6.1, the fundamental parallelogram has its lower left vertex at the origin. The point r is an integer point in the fundamental parallelogram. We often wish to know how many integer vectors $q$ are to be found in a fundamental parallelogram. A well-known algebraic theorem tells us that there are exactly

$$d = |\det B| \tag{6.3.5}$$

such points.[3] Let us denote these integer points by $q^1, q^2, \ldots, q^d$.

[3] See, Z. I. Borevich and I. R. Shafarevich, *Number Theory* (New York and London: Academic Press, 1966), Theorem 2 on pp. 85–87 and Lemma 1 on pp. 125–126. The proofs of Theorem 2 and Lemma 1 are constructive and show how to calculate the $d = \det B$

Now *any* integer vector $q$ can be associated with one of the points $q^j$ in the fundamental parallelogram in the following way: Since the columns of $B$ are linearly independent, an integer point $q$ can be written as some linear combination of the columns of $B$,

$$q = \sum_{i=1}^{n} B_i \cdot \lambda_i^*. \tag{6.3.6}$$

Let $[\lambda_i^*]$ be the largest integer which is less than or equal to $\lambda_i^*$. Then

$$\lambda_i^* = [\lambda_i^*] + (\lambda_i^* - [\lambda_i^*]) \tag{6.3.7}$$

where $(\lambda_i^* - [\lambda_i^*])$ is a non-negative fraction. Thus

$$q = \sum_{i=1}^{n} B_i \cdot [\lambda_i^*] + \sum_{i=1}^{n} B_i(\lambda_i^* - [\lambda_i^*]) \tag{6.3.8}$$

where

$$\sum_{i=1}^{n} B_i(\lambda_i^* - [\lambda_i^*]) = \{q\}_B \tag{6.3.9}$$

and where $\{q\}_B$ is an integer point in the fundamental parallelogram. Furthermore,

$$q - \{q\}_B = \sum_{i=1}^{n} B_i \cdot [\lambda_i^*] \tag{6.3.10}$$

and

$$q \equiv \{q\}_B \pmod{B}. \tag{6.3.11}$$

Whenever we write $\{q\}_B$ for an integer vector $q$ we are associating that vector with the corresponding point in the fundamental parallelogram.

Let us consider the following example:

$$B = \begin{bmatrix} 1 & 2 \\ 3 & 1 \end{bmatrix} \tag{6.3.12}$$

$$|\det B| = |1 - 6| = 5.$$

There are 5 points in the fundamental parallelogram. They are:

$$(0, 0), (1, 1), (1, 2), (2, 2), \text{and } (2, 3). \tag{6.3.13}$$

The $B$-lattice and the points of the fundamental parallelogram are shown in Figure 6.1.

---

integer vectors of the fundamental parallelogram using Gaussian eliminations (primal pivot steps of the revised simplex kind) combined with the Euclidean algorithm to find the greatest common divisor of a series of numbers. The reader is also referred to B. L. van der Waerden, *Modern Algebra* (New York: Fredrick Ungar and Co., 1950), Vol. 2, the "Elementary Divisor Theorem," pp. 107–109. The proof of this theorem is also constructive but its application to the problem of finding the integer vectors of a fundamental parallelogram is not quite so direct as Borevich and Shafarevich's Lemma 1.

Now consider the point $q = (15, 7)$. Since

$$B^{-1} = \begin{bmatrix} -\frac{1}{5} & \frac{2}{5} \\ \frac{3}{5} & -\frac{1}{5} \end{bmatrix} \tag{6.3.14}$$

we have

$$\begin{aligned} \lambda_1^* &= (-\tfrac{1}{5})\,15 + (\tfrac{2}{5})\,7 = -\tfrac{1}{5}, \\ \lambda_2^* &= (\tfrac{3}{5})\,15 + (-\tfrac{1}{5})\,7 = \tfrac{38}{5}, \\ [\lambda_1^*] &= -1, \qquad \lambda_1^* - [\lambda_1^*] = \tfrac{4}{5}, \\ [\lambda_2^*] &= 7, \quad \text{and} \quad \lambda_2^* - [\lambda_2^*] = \tfrac{3}{5}. \end{aligned} \tag{6.3.15}$$

Thus

$$\begin{aligned} \{q\}_B &= (1(\tfrac{4}{5}) + 2(\tfrac{3}{5}),\ 3(\tfrac{4}{5}) + 1(\tfrac{3}{5})) \\ &= (2, 3) \equiv (15, 7) \pmod{B}. \end{aligned} \tag{6.3.16}$$

## 6.4 The Modified Integer Programming Problem

Let us now take into account the integer restrictions on the $x_j$ variables. We wish to find an attainable point $z^* = y^* + r$ which maximizes (6.1.5) subject to (6.1.1), (6.1.2), and (6.1.4). For this purpose it will be convenient to work with the expression for $\pi$ in (6.2.5) which is equivalent to (6.1.5) when we have arbitrarily partitioned the $z$ and $y$ variables into $n$ basic and $m$ non-basic variables. Since the $x_j$ are required to be integer, from (6.1.1) and (6.1.4), the $z$ variables must also be integer. Thus the basic and non-basic variables are required to be non-negative and integer.

$$\begin{aligned} &a)\ w_i \geqq 0 \quad \text{and} \quad w_i \equiv 0 \pmod 1 \quad \text{for} \quad i = 1, \ldots, n; \text{ and} \\ &b)\ v_j \geqq 0 \quad \text{and} \quad v_j \equiv 0 \pmod 1 \quad \text{for} \quad j = 1, \ldots, m \end{aligned} \tag{6.4.1}$$

Now equations (6.2.6) and (6.4.1) are equivalent to (6.1.1), (6.1.2), and (6.1.4) where the $z$ and $x_j$ variables have been partitioned into basic and non-basic variables. Thus a profit-maximizing attainable point $z$ is one which maximizes (6.2.5) subject to (6.2.6) and (6.4.1). This problem will be called the original integer programming (IP) problem.

For the moment, however, let us simplify the problem somewhat by dropping the non-negativity restrictions on the *basic variables only*. This is called the modified IP problem in which we maximize

$$\pi = \pi_0 + \sum_{i=1}^{n} b_i \cdot w_i + \sum_{j=1}^{n} n_j \cdot v_j \tag{6.4.2}$$

subject to

$$\sum_{i=1}^{n} B_i \cdot w_i + \sum_{j=1}^{n} N_j \cdot v_j = r \tag{6.4.3}$$

and

$$\begin{aligned} &a) \quad w_i \equiv 0 \pmod 1, \quad \text{for} \quad i = 1, \ldots, n; \quad \text{and} \\ &b) \quad v_j \geqq 0 \quad \text{and} \quad v_j \equiv 0 \pmod 1, \quad \text{for} \quad j = 1, \ldots, m. \end{aligned} \tag{6.4.4}$$

In this section we discuss and prove several assertions concerning the modified IP problem. All of the propositions here assume that $B$ is an optimal basis[4] for some $r = r^*$, i.e., $\pi_j \leqq 0$ for $j = 1, \ldots, m$.

QI. If an optimal solution to the LP problem exists, then one exists for the original and modified IP problems for any integer vector $r$.
*Proof:* Suppose $z^0$ and $x_j^0$ for $j = 1, \ldots, m$ is an optimal solution to the LP problem. Then let

$$x_j^0 = [x_j^0] \tag{6.4.5}$$

where the $[x_j^0]$ are the largest integers less than or equal to the $x_j^0$. Then set

$$z^{00} = r - \sum_{j=1}^{m} A_j \cdot [x_j^0]. \tag{6.4.6}$$

The vector $z^{00}$ is integer since $r$ and $A_j$ are integer. Thus (6.2.2) or equivalently (6.4.3) has a feasible non-negative integer solution. This places a lower bound on the objective function (6.2.1) or equivalently (6.4.2) of

$$\pi^{00} = \pi_0 + \sum_{j=1}^{m} \pi_j \cdot [x_j^0]. \tag{6.4.7}$$

An upper bound can be formed from (6.2.11) which is also equivalent to (6.4.2) by setting $v_j = 0$ for $j = 1, \ldots, m$ since

$$\pi_j^0 = n_j - \sum_{k=1}^{n} p_k^0 \cdot n_{kj} \leqq 0.$$

The upper bound is

$$\pi^{**} = \pi_0 + \sum_{k=1}^{n} p_k^0 \cdot r_k = (p^0 + p) \cdot r. \tag{6.4.8}$$

Since the $A_j$ and the $x_j$ are integer, however, $\pi$ can assume only a finite number of values between the lower bound $\pi^{00}$ and the upper bound $\pi^{**}$ for non-negative integer-feasible solutions to (6.2.2). Thus if any non-negative, integer-feasible solution, $z'$ and $x'$, is better than another, $z''$ and $x''$, it must produce a value of $\pi''$ which is greater than $\pi'$ by a finite number always greater than some fixed $\varepsilon$. Thus there exists a non-negative, integer solution to (6.2.2) which produces a largest value of $\pi$. This shows that an optimal solution to the original IP problem exists.

[4] This is equivalent to the assumption that $B$ is dual feasible. See W. J. Baumol, *op.cit.*, pp. 116–121.

On the other hand, the modified IP problem can be expressed as a maximizing problem which is independent of the values of the basic variables $w_i$. To see this, note that if the $w_i$ are not restricted to be non-negative but can be any integers, (6.4.3) is equivalent to

$$\sum_{j=1}^{m} N_j \cdot v_j - r = \sum_{i=1}^{n} B_i \cdot (-w_i) \equiv 0 \pmod{B} \qquad (6.4.9)$$

or merely

$$\sum_{j=1}^{m} N_j \cdot v_j \equiv r \pmod{B}. \qquad (6.4.10)$$

That is, $\sum_{j=1}^{m} N_j \cdot v_j$ and $r$ differ by some integer linear combination of the columns of $B$. Now (6.4.2) is equivalent to (6.2.11) which contains none of the basic variables. The expression (6.4.10) is equivalent to (6.4.3) and (6.4.4a). Thus maximizing (6.2.11) subject to (6.4.10) and (6.4.4b) is equivalent to the modified IP problem and is independent of the basic variables. Then to prove the existence of a solution to the modified IP problem, we can use the same argument as with the original IP problem to show that an optimal solution exists.[5]

QII. If $r$ and $r + \Delta r$ are integer vectors, if

$$r \equiv (r + \Delta r) \pmod{B},$$

and if the basis $B$ is LP optimal for $r$ and $r + \Delta r$, then

$$\pi^*(r + \Delta r) = \pi^*(r) + p^* \cdot \Delta r,$$

where

$$p^* = p^0 + p$$

and $\pi^*(r)$ is the maximum value of $\pi$ in the modified IP problem.

*Proof:* If $r + \Delta r \equiv r \pmod{B}$ then

$$\sum_{j=1}^{m} N_j \cdot v_j \equiv r \equiv r + \Delta r \pmod{B}. \qquad (6.4.11)$$

[5] An alternative and generally greater lower bound on the objective function $\pi$ for the modified problem can be found by noting that any optimal solution $v_j^*$ $(j = 1, \ldots, m)$ for the modified problem satisfies the inequality

$$\sum_{j=1}^{m} v_j^* \leqq d - 1$$

where $d = |\det B|$. See R. Gomory, "On the Relation Between Integer and Non-Integer Solutions to Linear Programs," *Proceedings of the National Academy of Sciences*, Vol. 53 (Feb. 1965), pp. 260–265. Thus

$$\pi \geqq \pi^0 + p^0 \cdot r + (d - 1) \cdot \pi_j^0$$

where

$$\pi_j^0 = \min_{j=1,\cdots,m} (\pi_j^0).$$

Thus the set of solutions to the modified IP problem with resource vector $r$ is the same as those with $r + \Delta r$, i.e., (6.4.10) is satisfied for the same values of the $v_j$. Thus from (6.2.11) we see that

$$\pi^*(r) = (p + p^0)\cdot r + \sum_{j=1}^{m} \pi_j^0 \cdot v_j^*(r), \quad \text{and} \tag{6.4.12}$$

$$\pi^*(r + \Delta r) = (p + p^0)(r + \Delta r) + \sum_{j=1}^{m} \pi_j \cdot v_j^*(r) \tag{6.4.13}$$

where $v_j^*(r)$ is an optimal solution for the $v_j$ variables with resource vector $r$. Substracting (6.4.12) from (6.4.13), we obtain

$$\pi^*(r + \Delta r) = \pi^*(r) + (p + p^0)\cdot \Delta r. \tag{6.4.14}$$

Proposition QII may be compared to PVI in the linear programming case. If two resource vectors $r$ and $r + \Delta r$ differ by an integer linear combination of the basis vectors, then $p^*$ does in fact measure the marginal profitability of the increment $\Delta r$ in resources. In particular, if only one resource $r_i$ is changed then $\pi^*(r + \Delta r) = \pi^*(r) + p_i^* \cdot \Delta r_i$ and $p_i^* \cdot \Delta r_i$ is the marginal profitability of that resource.

Proposition QII may be illustrated geometrically with the aid of Figure 6.1. The integer linear combinations of $B_1$ and $B_2$ are corners of the parallelograms. When the resource vector $r$ is any such corner point, then $\pi^*(r) = p^* \cdot r$ as in proposition PVI. When $r$ and $r + \Delta r$ differ by an integer linear combination of the basis $B$, such as $r$ and $r'$ in Figure 6.1 then the *difference* between $\pi^*(r)$ and $\pi^*(r')$ is $p^*(r' - r)$, i.e., the change in resources valued at $p^0 + p$ where $p^0$ is the vector of dual prices.

For changes $\Delta r$ of the resource vector $r$ which are *not* integer linear combinations of the columns of $B$, however, we must resort to propositions QIII and QIV which follow:

QIII. If $r$ is an integer vector there exists a finite number $d = |\det B|$ of non-negative real numbers $S(\{r\}_B)$ where

$$\pi^*(r) = p^* \cdot r - S(\{r\}_B).$$

Geometrically, in Figure 6.2, positive integer linear combinations of $B_1$ and $B_2$ are corners of the parallelograms which lie in the cone spanned by the basis vectors $B_1$ and $B_2$. If $r$ is one of the corners of the parallelograms, then $\{r\}_B = 0$, and the linear programming problem has an integer solution and $\pi^*(r) = p^* \cdot r$. If $\{r\}_B$ is not zero, i.e., if the integer vector $r$ is not a corner of a parallelogram, the difference between the LP and modified IP optimal objective functions is $S(\{r\}_B)$. With each point $r$ inside a parallelogram we associate the subsidy $S(\{r\}_B)$ where $\{r\}_B$ lies in the fundamental parallelogram regardless of how "far out" we are in the cone spanned by $B_1$ and $B_2$.

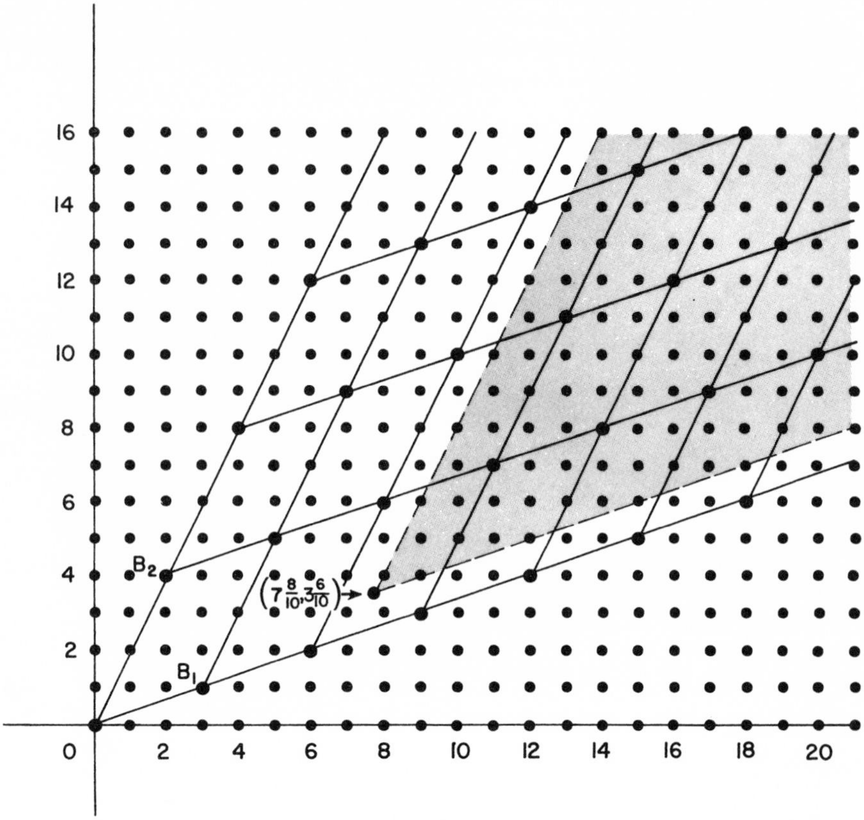


Figure 6.2

*Proof:* Let $v_j^*(\{r\}_B)$ be an optimal solution to the modified IP problem with resource vector $\{r\}_B$. Since $r \equiv \{r\}_B$ (mod $B$), from (6.4.10), we have

$$\sum_{j=1}^{m} N_j \cdot v_j^*(\{r\}_B) \equiv \{r\}_B \equiv r \text{ (mod } B). \qquad (6.4.15)$$

Since $v_j^*(\{r\}_B)$ is non-negative and integer, it certainly maximizes $\sum_{j=1}^{m} \pi_j^0 \cdot v_j$ subject to (6.4.3) and (6.4.4) and thus maximizes $\pi$ in (6.2.11) also. Therefore from (6.4.12)

$$\pi^*(r) = (p^0 + p)r - S(\{r\}_B) \qquad (6.4.16)$$

where

$$S(\{r\}_B) = -\sum_{j=1}^{m} \pi_j \cdot v_j^*(\{r\}_B). \qquad (6.4.17)$$

This proves proposition QIII.

Let us consider the following example as an illustration of QII and QIII. Let

$$\begin{aligned} -A_1 &= (11, -3, -1, -3), \\ -A_2 &= (14, -2, -4, -3), \\ -A_3 &= (2, 0, 0, -1), \\ p &= (1, 1, 1, 1), \end{aligned} \qquad (6.4.18)$$

$$r = (0, 28, 27, 36), \qquad (6.4.19)$$

$$\begin{aligned} y = (&11x_1 + 14x_2 + 2x_3, -3x_1 - 2x_2, -1x_1 - 4x_2, \\ &-3x_1 - 3x_2 - 1x_3), \end{aligned} \qquad (6.4.20)$$

$$\begin{aligned} z_1 &= 0 + 11x_1 + 14x_2 + 2x_3 \geqq 0, \\ z_2 &= 28 - 3x_1 - 2x_2 - 0x_3 \geqq 0, \\ z_3 &= 27 - 1x_1 - 4x_2 - 0x_3 \geqq 0, \quad \text{and} \\ z_4 &= 36 - 3x_1 - 3x_2 - 1x_3 \geqq 0. \end{aligned} \qquad (6.4.21)$$

The vector $z$ is attainable if

$$x_i \geqq 0 \quad \text{and} \quad x_i \equiv 0 \pmod 1, \quad \text{for} \quad i = 1, 2, 3; \quad \text{and} \qquad (6.4.22)$$

$$\pi = p \cdot z = p \cdot r - \sum_{j=1}^{3} p \cdot A_j \cdot x_j = 91 + 4x_1 + 5x_2 + 1x_3. \qquad (6.4.23)$$

The first constraint in (6.4.21) is redundant. For the sake of simplicity we will neglect it from here on. The same results would be obtained if we carried $z_1$ as a basic variable throughout the analysis. Let the basic and non-basic variables be given by

$$w_1 = x_1, w_2 = x_2, w_3 = x_3, v_1 = z_2, v_2 = z_3, \text{ and } v_3 = z_4. \qquad (6.4.24)$$

The basis $B$ is

$$B = \begin{bmatrix} 3 & 2 & 0 \\ 1 & 4 & 0 \\ 3 & 3 & 1 \end{bmatrix}. \qquad (6.4.25)$$

Solve (6.4.21) for the basic variables in terms of the non-basic variables.

$$\begin{aligned} w_1 &= 5\tfrac{8}{10} - \tfrac{4}{10}v_1 + \tfrac{2}{10}v_2 + 0v_3, \\ w_2 &= 5\tfrac{3}{10} + \tfrac{1}{10}v_1 - \tfrac{3}{10}v_2 + 0v_3, \quad \text{and} \\ w_3 &= 2\tfrac{7}{10} + \tfrac{9}{10}v_1 + \tfrac{3}{10}v_2 - 1v_3. \end{aligned} \qquad (6.4.26)$$

Substitute into (6.4.23) to get

$$\pi = 143\tfrac{4}{10} - \tfrac{2}{10}v_1 - \tfrac{4}{10}v_2 - 0v_3. \qquad (6.4.27)$$

The modified IP problem is to maximize (6.4.23) or equivalently (6.4.27) subject to

$$\begin{aligned} 1v_1 + 0v_2 + 0v_3 &= 28 - 3w_1 - 2w_2 - 0w_3, \\ 0v_1 + 1v_2 + 0v_3 &= 27 - 1w_1 - 4w_2 - 0w_3, \\ 0v_1 + 0v_2 + 1v_3 &= 36 - 3w_1 - 4w_2 - 1w_3; \end{aligned} \qquad (6.4.28)$$

and

$$\begin{aligned} &v_j \geqq 0 \quad \text{and} \quad v_j \equiv 0 \pmod 1 \quad \text{for} \quad j = 1, 2, 3; \quad \text{and} \\ &w_i \equiv 0 \pmod 1 \qquad\qquad\qquad \text{for} \quad i = 1, 2, 3. \end{aligned} \qquad (6.4.29)$$

An optimal solution to the modified problem is[6]

$$w_1^* = x_1^* = 6, \quad w_2^* = x_2^* = 5, \quad w_3^* = x_3^* = 3, \qquad (6.4.30)$$

$$\begin{aligned} v_1^* = z_1^* = 0, \quad v_2^* = z_2^* = 1, \quad v_3^* = z_3^* = 0, \quad \text{and} \\ \pi^* = 91 + 4.6 + 5.5 + 1.3 = 143. \end{aligned} \qquad (6.4.31)$$

Now suppose

$$\begin{aligned} \Delta r &= (10, 0, 0) \quad \text{and} \\ (r + \Delta r) &= (38, 27, 36). \end{aligned} \qquad (6.4.32)$$

The reader may verify that

$$r = (28, 27, 36) = 5B_1 + 5B_2 + 2B_3 + \tfrac{8}{10}B_1 + \tfrac{3}{10}B_2 + \tfrac{7}{10}B_3 \qquad (6.4.33)$$

and

$$(r + \Delta r) = (38, 27, 36) = 9B_1 + 4B_2 - 8B_3 + \tfrac{8}{10}B_1 + \tfrac{3}{10}B_2 + \tfrac{7}{10}B_3. \qquad (6.4.34)$$

Since the difference between $r$ and $r + \Delta r$ is an integer linear combination of the columns of $B$, it follows that $r \equiv r + \Delta r \pmod B$ and QII may be applied. The dual prices are

$$p_1^0 = \tfrac{2}{10}, p_2^0 = \tfrac{4}{10}, \quad \text{and} \quad p_3^0 = 1; \qquad (6.4.35)$$

and

$$p^* = p + p^0 = (1\tfrac{2}{10}, 1\tfrac{4}{10}, 2). \qquad (6.4.36)$$

[6] For methods of solving the modified problem see R. Gomory, *ibid.*, p. 260 and C. R. Frank, Jr., "Parametric Programming in Integers," in *Methods of Operations Research* (Meisenheim: Verlag Anton Hain, 1967), pp. 167–181. Gomory suggests a dynamic programming algorithm to solve the modified problem for different values of $r$. Frank works with a version of the Gomory cutting plane technique (See R. Gomory, "Outline of an Algorithm for Integer Solutions to Linear Programs." *Bulletin of the American Mathematical Society*, Vol. 64, September 1958 or W. J. Baumol, *op.cit.*, pp. 148–166). in which the constant terms of the Gomory cutting planes are altered with changes in $r$ by means of a recursive relationship.

Now from proposition QII,

$$\pi^*(r + \Delta r) = \pi^*(r) + p^* \cdot \Delta r = 143 + 12 = 155. \qquad (6.4.37)$$

It is possible to show that an optimal solution to the modified IP problem for $r + \Delta r$ is

$$\begin{aligned} w_1^* &= 10, \quad w_2^* = 4, \quad w_3^* = -6, \\ v_1^* &= 0, \quad v_2^* = 1, \quad \text{and} \quad v_3^* = 0. \end{aligned} \qquad (6.4.38)$$

From (6.4.17) and (6.4.27) we have

$$S(\{r + \Delta r\}_B) = 0 \cdot \tfrac{2}{10} + 1 \cdot \tfrac{4}{10} + 0 \cdot 0 = \tfrac{4}{10}. \qquad (6.4.39)$$

Thus according to QIII

$$\pi^*(r + \Delta r) = p^* \cdot (r + \Delta r) - \tfrac{4}{10} = 155\tfrac{4}{10} - \tfrac{4}{10} = 155 \qquad (6.4.40)$$

where $p^*$ is given by (6.4.36) and $r + \Delta r$ by (6.4.32).

The $d$ different non-negative number $S(\{r\}_B)$ mentioned in proposition QIII correspond to the $d = |\det B| = 10$ different values of $\{r\}_B$. These values may be generated in a number of different ways which to spare the reader's time and patience will not be described here.[7] Suffice to say that the 10 different values for $\{r\}_B$ are as follows:

$$\begin{aligned} (3, 2, 4) &= \tfrac{8}{10}B_1 + \tfrac{3}{10}B_2 + \tfrac{7}{10}B_3, \\ (3, 3, 4) &= \tfrac{6}{10}B_1 + \tfrac{6}{10}B_2 + \tfrac{4}{10}B_3, \\ (3, 4, 4) &= \tfrac{4}{10}B_1 + \tfrac{9}{10}B_2 + \tfrac{1}{10}B_3, \\ (1, 1, 2) &= \tfrac{2}{10}B_1 + \tfrac{2}{10}B_2 + \tfrac{8}{10}B_3, \\ (1, 2, 2) &= 0B_1 + \tfrac{5}{10}B_2 + \tfrac{5}{10}B_3, \\ (4, 4, 5) &= \tfrac{8}{10}B_1 + \tfrac{8}{10}B_2 + \tfrac{2}{10}B_3, \\ (2, 1, 3) &= \tfrac{6}{10}B_1 + \tfrac{1}{10}B_2 + \tfrac{9}{10}B_3, \\ (2, 2, 3) &= \tfrac{4}{10}B_1 + \tfrac{4}{10}B_2 + \tfrac{6}{10}B_3, \\ (2, 3, 3) &= \tfrac{2}{10}B_1 + \tfrac{7}{10}B_2 + \tfrac{3}{10}B_3, \quad \text{and} \\ (0, 0, 0) &= 0B_1 + 0B_2 + 0B_3. \end{aligned} \qquad (6.4.41)$$

[7] As mentioned above, Borevich and Shafarevich and van der Waerden give constructive proofs so that the different values of $\{r\}_B$ can be determined. Another method is to multiply each column of the inverse of $B$ by an integer $t$ where $t$ runs from 1 through $d = |\det B|$. Then the vector of non-negative fractional parts of each resulting vector is determined. This process is repeated with each column of $B$ successively until $d$ different vectors of fractional parts are determined. Each of these fractional vectors is multiplied by the matrix $B$ to produce the $d$ different values of $\{r\}_B$.

The solutions to the modified problems for these ten values of $\{r\}_B$ and the number $S(\{r\}_B)$ calculated from (6.4.17) are:

| $\{r\}_B$ | $v_1^*$ | $v_2^*$ | $v_3^*$ | $S(\{r\}_B)$ |
|---|---|---|---|---|
| $r^1 = (3, 2, 4)$ | 0 | 1 | 0 | $\frac{4}{10}$ |
| $r^2 = (3, 3, 4)$ | 4 | 0 | 0 | $\frac{8}{10}$ |
| $r^3 = (3, 4, 4)$ | 1 | 0 | 0 | $\frac{2}{10}$ |
| $r^4 = (1, 1, 2)$ | 1 | 1 | 0 | $\frac{6}{10}$ |
| $r^5 = (1, 2, 2)$ | 5 | 0 | 0 | 1 |
| $r^6 = (4, 4, 5)$ | 2 | 0 | 0 | $\frac{4}{10}$ |
| $r^7 = (2, 1, 3)$ | 2 | 1 | 0 | $\frac{8}{10}$ |
| $r^8 = (2, 2, 3)$ | 6 | 0 | 0 | $\frac{12}{10}$ |
| $r^9 = (2, 3, 3)$ | 3 | 0 | 0 | $\frac{6}{10}$ |
| $r^{10} = (0, 0, 0)$ | 0 | 0 | 0 | 0 |

(6.4.42)

Thus if $r = (43, 19, 32)$, we have

$$(43, 19, 32) = 13B_1 + 1B_2 - 13B_3 + \tfrac{4}{10}B_1 + \tfrac{4}{10}B_2 + \tfrac{6}{10}B_3 \qquad (6.4.43)$$

and from (6.4.41)

$$(43, 19, 32) \equiv (2, 2, 3) \pmod{B}. \qquad (6.4.44)$$

From proposition QIII, (6.4.16), (6.4.36) and (6.4.42), it follows that

$$\pi^*(43, 19, 32) = 142\tfrac{2}{10} - \tfrac{12}{10} = 141. \qquad (6.4.45)$$

Proposition QIII leads directly to

QIV. If $r$ and $r + \Delta r$ are integer, then

$$\pi^*(r + \Delta r) = \pi^*(r) + p^* \cdot \Delta r + Q(\{\Delta r\}_B, \{r\}_B)$$

where

$$Q(\{\Delta r\}_B, \{r\}_B) = S(\{r\}_B) - S(\{r + \Delta r\}_B)$$

can only assume a finite number $d!$ of values where $d = |\det B|$ and

$$Q(\{\Delta r\}_B, \{r\}_B) = 0 \quad \text{if} \quad \Delta r \equiv 0 \pmod{B}.$$

Propositions QIII and QIV may be compared to PV and PVI in the LP case. QIII says that the maximum profit is equal to resources valued at prices $p^*$ less a subsidy $S(\{r\}_B)$. QIV says that the marginal profitability of an increase of $\Delta r$ in resources is equal to $p^* \cdot \Delta r$ plus an adjustment factor $Q(\{\Delta r\}_B, \{r\}_B)$, which in fact may be either positive or negative. There are a finite number $d!$ where $d = |\det B|$ such adjustment factors and any particular adjustment factor is dependent both on the change $\Delta r$ in resources as well as original resource vector $r$. In the special case, however, where $\Delta r \equiv 0 \pmod{B}$, the adjustment factor is zero which, of course, is implied by proposition QII.

As an illustration of QIV, suppose

$$\begin{aligned} r &= (3, 2, 4), \quad \text{and} \\ r + \Delta r &= (3, 3, 4). \end{aligned} \tag{6.4.46}$$

Using (6.4.42), we have

$$\begin{aligned} S(\{r\}_B) &= \tfrac{4}{10}, \\ S(\{r + \Delta r\}_B) &= \tfrac{8}{10}, \quad \text{and} \\ S(\{r\}_B) - S(\{r + \Delta r\}_B) &= -\tfrac{4}{10} \end{aligned} \tag{6.4.47}$$

From proposition QIII and (6.4.36), we get

$$\begin{aligned} \pi^*(r) &= (p^* \cdot r - S(\{r\}_B) \\ &= (\tfrac{12}{10}) \cdot 3 + (\tfrac{14}{10}) \cdot 2 + 2 \cdot 4 - \tfrac{4}{10} \\ &= 14. \end{aligned} \tag{6.4.48}$$

From proposition QIV and (6.4.47), we have

$$\begin{aligned} \pi^*(r + \Delta r) &= 14 + p^*(0, 1, 0) - \tfrac{4}{10} \\ &= 14 + \tfrac{14}{10} - \tfrac{4}{10} \\ &= 15. \end{aligned} \tag{6.4.49}$$

## 6.5 The Original Integer Programming Problem

The original integer programming problem was to maximize (6.4.2) subject to (6.4.3) and (6.4.1). The modified problem neglected the non-negativity conditions on basic variables $w_i$. Thus the modified problem is to maximize (6.4.2) subject to (6.4.3) and (6.4.4). In this section we investigate the conditions under which a solution to the modified IP problem is also a solution to the original problem and the implications of this equivalence, when it occurs.

The vector $\{r\}_B$ assumes a finite number $d$ of values $r^1, r^2, \ldots, r^d$. If $v_j^*(r^s)$ for $j = 1, \ldots, m$ is an optimal solution to the *modified* integer programming problem, then from (6.2.8), we have

$$w_i = \sum_{k=1}^{n} b_{ik}^{-1} \cdot r_k - \sum_{j=1}^{n} \pi_{ij} \cdot v_j \quad \text{for } i = 1, \ldots, n \tag{6.5.1}$$

where

$$\pi_{ij} = \sum_{k=1}^{n} b_{ik}^{-k} \cdot n_{kj}. \tag{6.5.2}$$

Now the $w_i$ are non-negative if

$$\sum_{k=1}^{n} b_{ik}^{-1} \cdot r_k \geqq \sum_{j=1}^{n} \pi_{ij} \cdot v_j^*(r^s) = \alpha_i(r^s) \tag{6.5.3}$$

$$\text{for } i = 1, \ldots, n \quad \text{and} \quad s = 1, 2, \ldots, d.$$

Let

$$\alpha_i^* = \max_s \, [\alpha_i(r^s)]. \tag{6.5.4}$$

Then (6.5.3) holds if

$$\sum b_{ik}^{-1} \cdot v_k \geqq \alpha_i^* \quad \text{for } i = 1, \ldots, n. \tag{6.5.5}$$

Now let us translate the cone

$$r = \sum_{i=1}^{n} B_i \cdot q_i \quad \text{and} \quad q_i \geqq 0 \quad \text{for } i = 1, \ldots, n \tag{6.5.6}$$

to the point $\sum_{i=1}^{n} B_i \cdot \alpha_i^* = b^*$. This translated cone is the set of points $r$ satisfying

$$r = \sum_{i=1}^{n} B_i \cdot q_i + b^* \quad \text{and} \quad q_i \geqq 0 \quad \text{for } i = 1, \ldots, n. \tag{6.5.7}$$

If we solve (6.5.7) for $q_i$, we see that for any point $r$ which lies in this translated cone, (6.5.5) and (6.5.3) are satisfied and the basic variables $w_i$ can be made non-negative for all such values of $r$. The translated cone (6.5.7) will be denoted by $R$. It lies in the interior of the cone (6.5.6) generated by the columns of $B$.[8] We have proved the following proposition:

RI. If $r$ is integer and lies in the translated cone $R$, there exists an optimal solution $w_i^*(r)$ and $v_j^*(r)$ to the modified IP problem which is also a solution to the original IP problem.

Furthermore

RII. If $r$ and $r + \Delta r$ are integer and belong to $R$ the translated cone, then propositions QI through QIV apply to the original IP problem as well as the modified IP problem.

Let us illustrate RI and RII with the example in (6.4.18) through (6.4.22). If we solve for the basic variables in terms of the non-basic

[8] A translated cone in the interior of the cone generated by the columns of $B$ is also defined by Gomory ("On the Relation Between Integer and Non-Integer Solutions to Linear Programs"). Gomory's cone is defined without reference to the solutions to the modified IP problems, but depends only on the non-basic activity vectors. Gomory's cone, however, provides a very weak sufficient condition for Propositions RI through RIII. There are several other ways to provide stronger sufficient conditions (i.e., cones which always contain the Gomory cone) which require no more information. The cone defined here, however, which requires that a set of solutions to all modified IP problems be known, provides a much stronger sufficiency condition.

variables we get (6.4.26), which is analogous to (6.5.1). [The breakdown into basic and non-basic variables and the basis vectors are given in (6.4.24) and (6.4.25)]. Now (6.4.42) gives us a set of solutions for the non-basic variables. From (6.5.3) and (6.5.4), we have the following:

| $s$ | $\alpha_1(r^s)$ | $\alpha_2(r^s)$ | $\alpha_3(r^s)$ |
|---|---|---|---|
| 1 | $-\frac{2}{10}$ | $+\frac{3}{10}$ | $-\frac{3}{10}$ |
| 2 | $+\frac{16}{10}$ | $-\frac{4}{10}$ | $-\frac{36}{10}$ |
| 3 | $+\frac{4}{10}$ | $-\frac{1}{10}$ | $-\frac{9}{10}$ |
| 4 | $+\frac{2}{10}$ | $+\frac{2}{10}$ | $-\frac{12}{10}$ |
| 5 | $+\frac{20}{10}$ | $-\frac{5}{10}$ | $-\frac{45}{10}$ |
| 6 | $+\frac{8}{10}$ | $-\frac{2}{10}$ | $-\frac{18}{10}$ |
| 7 | $+\frac{6}{10}$ | $+\frac{1}{10}$ | $-\frac{21}{10}$ |
| 8 | $+\frac{24}{10}$ | $-\frac{6}{10}$ | $-\frac{54}{10}$ |
| 9 | $+\frac{12}{10}$ | $-\frac{3}{10}$ | $-\frac{27}{10}$ |
| 10 | 0 | 0 | 0 |

(6.5.8)

Thus

$$\alpha_1^* = \tfrac{24}{10}, \quad \alpha_2^* = \tfrac{3}{10}, \quad \alpha_3^* = 0, \qquad b^* = (7\tfrac{8}{10}, 3\tfrac{6}{10}, 8\tfrac{1}{10}). \tag{6.5.9}$$

The cone $R$ is the set of points $r$ satisfying

$$r = B_1 \cdot q_1 + B_2 \cdot q_2 + B_3 \cdot q_3 + (7\tfrac{8}{10}, 3\tfrac{6}{10}, 8\tfrac{1}{10}) \text{ and } q_i \geqq 0 \quad \text{for } i = 1, 2, 3. \tag{6.5.10}$$

A projection of this translated cone is shown in Figure 6.2 in two dimensions $r_1$ and $r_2$. The projected basis vectors (see (6.4.25)) $B_1$ and $B_2$ are shown with the cone spanned by these vectors lying in between the two rays through $B_1$ and $B_2$. Now the point $(b_1^*, b_2^*) = (7\frac{8}{10}, 3\frac{6}{10})$ lies inside this cone. The projection of the translated cone $R$ is the shaded area. It has sides parallel to the rays $B_1$ and $B_2$ and emanates from the point $b^* = (b_1^*, b_2^*)$. For any integer $r$ inside the cone $R$, the IP problem and the modified IP problem have at least one identical optimal solution. If $r$ lies in $R$, then propositions QI through QIV apply to the original IP problem. Furthermore, we have the following proposition:

RIII. If $r$ is integer and lies in $R$, and if $z^* = r + y^*$ is a profit maximizing attainable point (i.e., a solution to the original IP problem), then there exist a finite number $d = |\det B|$ of numbers $S(\{y\}_B)$ such that $0 = p^* \cdot y^* + S(\{y^*\}_B) \geqq p^* \cdot y + S(\{y\}_B)$ for all $y \in Y$.

This last proposition is the analog of PIV in the linear programming case. The profit of the efficient possible point $y^*$ is at a maximum if we value the profit of any point $y$ as follows:

$$\pi(y) = p^* \cdot y + S(\{y\}_B) \tag{6.5.11}$$

That is, $y$ is the product of the price vector $p^*$ and $y$ (the usual profit definition) plus a subsidy $S(\{y\}_B)$ which assumes a finite number of values. The subsidy $S(\{y\}_B)$ is calculated as follows:

$$-S(\{y\}_B) = \text{Max}\left(-\sum_{j=1}^{m_1} p^* \cdot A_j^N \cdot x_j^N\right) \tag{6.5.12}$$

subject to

$$\sum_{j=1}^{m_1} A_j^N \cdot x_j^N \equiv \{-y\}_B \pmod{B}, \qquad x_j^N \geqq 0, \quad \text{and} \quad x_j^N \equiv 0 \pmod{1} \quad \text{for } j = 1, \ldots, m_1 \tag{6.5.13}$$

where the $x_j$ variables and activities $A_j$ have been divided into $m_1$ of them $x_j^N$ and $A_j^N$ which are non-basic and $m - m_1$ of them $x_j^B$ and $A_j^B$ which are basic.

*Proof:* For any possible point $y$ we have

$$-y = \sum_{j=1}^{m_1} A_j^N \cdot x_j^N + \sum_{j=1}^{m-m_1} A_j^B \cdot x_j^B, \qquad x_j^N \geqq 0, \quad x_j^N \equiv 0 \pmod{1}, \qquad x_j^B \geqq 0, \quad \text{and} \quad x_j^B \equiv 0 \pmod{1} \quad \text{for } j = 1, \ldots, m. \tag{6.5.14}$$

The set of points satisfying (6.5.14), however certainly satisfies (6.5.13) since $-y$ and $\sum_{j=1}^{m_1} A_j^N \cdot x_j^N$ differ by an integer linear combination of columns of $B$. Thus for any possible point

$$-\sum_{j=1}^{m_1} p^* \cdot A_j^N \cdot x_j^N \leqq -S(\{y\}_B). \tag{6.5.15}$$

From (6.5.11), for any possible point $y$

$$\pi(y) = -p^* \cdot \sum_{j=1}^{m-m_1} A_j^B \cdot x_j^B + -p^* \cdot \sum_{j=1}^{m_1} A_j^N \cdot x_j^N + S(\{y\}_B). \tag{6.5.16}$$

From proposition PI, $p^* \cdot A_j^B = 0$ and from (6.5.15)

$$\pi(y) \leqq 0 \quad \text{for all } y \in Y. \tag{6.5.17}$$

Let us divide the vector $z$ into a vector $z_B$ of basic components and a vector $z_N$ of non-basic components (i.e., $(z_B, z_N) = z$). From (6.5.14) we may write (6.5.13) as follows:

$$\sum_{j=1}^{m_1} A_j^N \cdot x_j^N \equiv -y = -z + r \pmod{B} \qquad (6.5.18)$$

or

$$\sum_{j=1}^{m_1} A_j^N \cdot x_j^N + z_N \equiv z_B + r \pmod{B} \equiv r \pmod{B} \qquad (6.5.19)$$

or

$$\sum_{j=1}^{m} N_j \cdot v_j \equiv r \pmod{B}. \qquad (6.5.20)$$

Thus (6.5.13) is equivalent to (6.4.10) which is equivalent to (6.4.3) and (6.4.4).

Let us now fix the value of $z_N$ at its original IP optimal value $z_N^*$. Next add $-p^0 \cdot z_N^* + p^* \cdot r$ to both sides of (6.5.12).

$$\begin{aligned} p^* \cdot r - p^0 \cdot z_N^* - S(\{y\}_B) \\ &= p^* \cdot r - p^0 \cdot z_N^* + \text{Max}\left(-\sum_{j=1}^{m_1} p^* \cdot A_j^N \cdot x_j^N\right) \qquad (6.5.21) \\ &= \text{Max}\left(\pi_o + p^0 \cdot r - p^0 \cdot z_N^* - \sum_{j=1}^{m_1} p^* \cdot A_j^N \cdot x_j^N\right) \end{aligned}$$

In our discussion of PI and PII, we demonstrated that

$$\begin{aligned} \pi_j^0 &= n_j - \sum_{k=1}^{n} p_k^0 \cdot n_{kj} = -p^* \cdot A_j^N, \quad \text{if } v_j = x^N, \quad \text{and} \\ \pi_j^0 &= -p_j^0. \qquad\qquad\qquad\qquad\quad \text{if } v_j = z_j^N. \end{aligned} \qquad (6.5.22)$$

Thus by maximizing (6.4.2) (subject to (6.4.3) and (6.4.4)), we also maximize (6.5.12) subject to (6.5.13). Therefore some solution to the modified IP problem (and since $r$ lies in $R$, to the original IP problem) is also a solution to (6.5.12) subject to (6.4.13). An optimal solution to (6.5.12) and (6.5.13) then is $(x_j^N)^*$ for $j = 1, \ldots, m_1$ which are optimal values of $x_j^N$ for the original IP problem and

$$-\sum_{j=1}^{m_1} p^* \cdot A_j^N \cdot (x_j^N)^* = -S(\{y^*\}_B) \qquad (6.5.23)$$

From proposition PI and (6.5.15), we have

$$\pi(y^*) = 0 \qquad (6.5.24)$$

and proposition RIII is proved.

From proposition RIII it follows that

$$0 \geqq p^* \cdot y^* \geqq -S(\{y^*\}_B) \tag{6.5.25}$$

and from PIV

$$p^* \cdot y \leqq 0 \quad \text{for all } y \in Y. \tag{6.5.26}$$

Thus we might say that $y^*$ is "almost" profit-maximizing. Furthermore the subsidies $S(\{y\}_B)$ are finite in number and non-negative so, of course, they have a least upper bound $S^*$.[9] If $r$ belongs to $R$, certainly for $\lambda \geqq 1$, $\lambda \cdot r$ belongs to $R$. So if $z^*(\lambda r) = \lambda \cdot r + y^*(\lambda r)$ is a profit-maximizing attainable point, then

$$\begin{aligned} 0 \geqq p \cdot y^*(\lambda r) &\geqq -S^* \quad \text{for } \lambda \geqq 1 \quad \text{and} \\ 0 \geqq p \cdot y & \qquad\quad\;\; \text{for } y \in Y. \end{aligned} \tag{6.5.27}$$

Thus for any increase in scale of the resources, no matter how large, the loss never exceeds the amount of the maximum possible subsidy $S^*$.

Let us illustrate RIII with the example as outlined in (6.4.18) to (6.4.23) with the exception that we add a fourth activity

$$-A_4 = (12, -3, -2, -4). \tag{6.5.28}$$

An optimal solution is

$$\begin{aligned} & w_1^* = x_1^* = 6,\ w_2^* = x_2^* = 5,\ w_3^* = x_3^* = 3, \quad \text{and} \\ & w_4^* = z_1^* = 142; \\ \text{and} \quad & \\ & v_1^* = z_2^* = 0,\ v_2^* = z_3^* = 1,\ v_3^* = z_4^* = 0, \quad \text{and} \\ & v_4^* = x_4^* = 0. \end{aligned} \tag{6.5.29}$$

The basis $B$ is

$$B = \begin{bmatrix} -11 & -14 & -2 & 1 \\ 3 & 2 & 0 & 0 \\ 1 & 4 & 0 & 0 \\ 3 & 3 & 1 & 0 \end{bmatrix}. \tag{6.5.30}$$

$$\begin{aligned} y_1^* &= +11x_1^* + 14x_2^* + 2x_3^* = +142, \\ y_2^* &= -3x_1^* - 2x_2^* - 0x_3^* = -28, \\ y_3^* &= -1x_1^* - 4x_2^* - 0x_3^* = -26, \quad \text{and} \\ y_4^* &= -3x_1^* - 3x_2^* - 1x_3^* = -36; \quad \text{and} \end{aligned} \tag{6.5.31}$$

$$-y^* = (-142, +28, +26, +36) = 6B_1 + 5B_2 + 3B_3 + 0B_4. \tag{6.5.32}$$

[9] The least upper bound on the subsidies $S(\{y\}_B)$ is no larger than the difference between an upper and lower bound on the objective function of the modified IP problem. An upper bound is $\pi = 0$. A good lower bound was described above in Footnote 5.

Thus

$$\{y^*\}_B = 0. \tag{6.5.33}$$

Since $p^* \cdot A_j^N \leqq 0$ for $j = 1, \ldots, m_1$, from (6.5.12) and (6.5.13) we see that

$$S(\{y^*\}_B) = 0. \tag{6.5.34}$$

From (6.4.18) and (6.4.35), proposition RIII says

$$-p^* \cdot y^* = (1, \tfrac{12}{10}, \tfrac{14}{10}, 2) \cdot (-142, 28, 26, 36) = 0. \tag{6.5.35}$$

On the other hand, let us take any other possible point $y$, say

$$y = -11 \cdot A_4 = 11 \cdot (12, -3, -2, -4). \tag{6.5.36}$$

Then

$$-y = 2\tfrac{8}{10}B_1 + 2\tfrac{3}{10}B_2 - 1\tfrac{3}{10}B_3 + 72\tfrac{4}{10}B_4 \tag{6.5.37}$$

and

$$\begin{aligned} \{-y\}_B &= \tfrac{8}{10}B_1 + \tfrac{3}{10}B_2 + \tfrac{7}{10}B_3 + \tfrac{4}{10}B_4 \\ &= (-14, 3, 2, 4). \end{aligned} \tag{6.5.38}$$

Thus, the subsidy $S(\{y\}_B)$ is (from (6.5.12) and (6.5.13)):

$$-S(\{y^*\}_B) = \text{Max}\,[-p^* \cdot A_4 \cdot x_4] = \text{Max}\,(-3\tfrac{4}{10}x_4) \tag{6.5.39}$$

subject to

$$\begin{aligned} (-12x_4, 3x_4, 2x_4, 4x_4) &\equiv (-14, 3, 2, 4) \quad (\text{mod } B), \\ x_4 \geqq 0, \quad &\text{and} \quad x_4 \equiv 0 \quad (\text{mod } 1). \end{aligned} \tag{6.5.40}$$

It is easy to show that an optimal solution to this problem is

$$x_4^* = 1, \quad \text{and} \quad S(\{y\}_B) = 3\tfrac{4}{10}. \tag{6.5.41}$$

Furthermore

$$\begin{aligned} \pi(y) &= p^* \cdot y + S(\{y\}_B) = p^* \cdot 11 \cdot (12, -3, -2, -4) + 3\tfrac{4}{10} \\ &= -37\tfrac{4}{10} - 3\tfrac{4}{10} = -34 \end{aligned} \tag{6.5.42}$$

This profit is negative. For any other possible point $y$, the profit is non-positive. The reader may verify that the profits associated with $y^*$, using (6.5.11), are zero. Thus $y^*$ is a profit-maximizing possible point.

Since there is only a finite number $d = |\det B|$ of subsidies, these can be calculated in advance,[10] for all possible values of $\{y\}_B$. Then the implementation of such a pricing scheme would require a seller to have a list of the possible values of $\{y\}_B$ and a corresponding list of subsidies. The determination of the sale price of a group $y^0$ of commodities would require that group to be broken up into two components,

$$(\{y^0\}_B) \quad \text{and} \quad (y^0 - \{y^0\}_B).$$

[10] As was indicated in our discussion of Proposition RIII, the calculation of the subsidies is equivalent to calculating all possible $d$ solutions to the modified IP problem. See Footnote 6 above.

The first component would sell as a group at a price $p^* \cdot \{y^0\}_B + S\{y^0\}_B$. The second group of commodities would be priced individually at $p_i^*$ for $i = 1, \ldots, n$. This scheme of pricing in some cases is similar to a method of odd-lot pricing scheme.

## 6.6 Odd-Lot Pricing

Suppose

$$-A_1 = (5, -4), \quad -A_2 = (6, -7), \quad -A_3 = (3, -3), \tag{6.6.1}$$

$$p = (0, 1), \quad \text{and} \quad r = (-11, 50). \tag{6.6.2}$$

Then the original IP problem is to determine

$$\text{Max } (-4x_1 - 7x_2 - 3x_3) \tag{6.6.3}$$

subject to

$$\begin{aligned} z_1 &= r_1 + y_1 = 5x_1 + 6x_2 + 3x_3 - 11 \geqq 0, \\ z_2 &= r_2 + y_2 = -4x_1 - 7x_2 - 3x_3 + 50 \geqq 0, \end{aligned} \tag{6.6.4}$$

$$x_i \geqq 0, \quad \text{and} \quad x_i \equiv 0 \pmod 1 \quad \text{for} \quad i = 1, 2, 3. \tag{6.6.5}$$

The second constraint in (6.6.4) is not binding so that the problem can be viewed as the minimization of the cost of producing at least 11 units of commodity 1.

A profit-maximizing attainable point is

$$\begin{aligned} z^* &= (0, 40), \ (x_1^*, x_2^*, x_3^*) = (1, 0, 2), \quad \text{and} \\ y^* &= -1 \cdot A_1 - 0 \cdot A_2 - 2 \cdot A_3 = (11, -10). \end{aligned} \tag{6.6.6}$$

Now an optimal LP basis is

$$B = \begin{bmatrix} 5 & 0 \\ -4 & 1 \end{bmatrix} \quad \text{where} \quad d = |\det B| = 5. \tag{6.6.7}$$

The 5 different possible values of $\{y\}_B$ with their associated subsidies are

| $\{y\}_B$ | $S(\{y\}_B)$ |
|---|---|
| (1, 0) | $\frac{6}{5}$ |
| (2, 0) | $\frac{7}{5}$ |
| (3, 0) | $\frac{3}{5}$ |
| (4, 0) | $\frac{4}{5}$ |
| (0, 0) | 0 |

(6.6.8)

The prices are

$$p^0 = (\tfrac{4}{5}, 0), \quad \text{and} \qquad p^* = p^0 + p = (\tfrac{4}{5}, 1). \tag{6.6.9}$$

Now let us take the possible point $y^* = (y_1^*, y_2^*)$. We price the first commodity as follows: Find the largest multiple of $d = 5$ which is less than $y_1^*$ (the number of full lots). Subtract this from $y_1^*$ to find the size $\{y_1^*\}_5$ of the odd lot. The full lots are priced at $d \cdot p_1^0 = 5 \cdot \frac{4}{5} = 4$. The odd lot is priced as a group at $p_1^0 \cdot \{y_1^*\}_5 + S(\{y_1^*\}_5, 0)$. Thus since $y_1^* = 11$, there are two full lots which are priced at 4 and $2 \cdot 4 = 8$ is the revenue from these full lots. The revenue from the odd lot of size 1 is $\frac{4}{5} \cdot 1 + S(1, 0) = \frac{4}{5} + \frac{6}{5} = 2$. Thus total revenue is $8 + 2 = 10$.

Now $y_2^*$ is priced at the price $p_2^* = 1$. So that $p_2^* \cdot y_2^* = -10$. Thus revenue equals cost and profit is equal to zero. For any other possible point $y$, the profit is non-positive so that $y^*$ is profit-maximizing.

## 6.7 Discriminatory Pricing

Instead of specifying a single price vector, let us define a discriminatory pricing system in which each resource has two prices, one price up to a given amount and another price thereafter. Let $y^* = z^* - r$ be an optimal integer solution to the original integer programming problem, i.e., $z^* = r + y^*$ is a profit-maximizing attainable point. Let $p^0$ be the vector of *linear* programming dual prices. Then the price vector $p^*$ is defined as

$$\begin{aligned} p_i^* &= p_i^0 + p_i + v_i, \quad \text{if } y_i \leqq y_i^*; \quad \text{and} \\ p_i^* &= p_i^0 + p_i, \qquad\quad \text{if } y_i > y_i^*. \end{aligned} \tag{6.7.1}$$

Let $I_A$ be the set of indices $i$ for which $y_i > y_i^*$ and $I_B$ is the set of indices $i$ for which $y_i \leqq y_i^*$. Then using the definition of profit in Chapter 4, we have

$$\begin{aligned} \pi(y) &= \pi(y^*) + \sum_{i \in I_A} (p_i^0 + p_i) \cdot (y_i - y_i^*) + \sum_{i \in I_B} (p_i^0 + p_i + v_i) \cdot (y_i - y_i^*) \\ &= \pi(y^*) + (p^0 + p) \cdot (y - y^*) + \sum_{i \in I_B} v_i \cdot (y_i - y_i^*). \end{aligned} \tag{6.7.2}$$

Then we have

RIV. There exists a set of discriminatory prices $p^* = p^0 + p > 0$ such that $\pi(y^*) \geqq \pi(y)$ for all possible points $y$ where $z^* = r + y^*$ is a profit-maximizing attainable point given the set of prices $p$.

*Proof:* The point $y^*$ is efficient. Thus $y_i > y_i^*$ for at least one $i$ unless $y = y^*$. Thus

$$\sum_{i \in I_B} v_i \cdot (y_i - y_i^*) \leqq - \min_i (v_i) = -v \tag{6.7.3}$$

since $y_i$ and $y_i^*$ must differ by at least an integer. From proposition RIII,

$$(p^0 + p)\cdot y^* \geqq - s \tag{6.7.4}$$

where $s$ is some non-negative real number. Furthermore from proposition RIII,

$$(p^0 + p)\cdot y \leqq 0. \tag{6.7.5}$$

Combining these three inequalities with (6.7.2) we have

$$\pi(y) - \pi(y^*) \leqq s - v. \tag{6.7.6}$$

Thus if we set

$$\min_i (v_i) = s, \tag{6.7.7}$$

it follows that

$$\pi(y) - \pi(y^*) \leqq 0. \tag{6.7.8}$$

## 6.8 Conclusions

In this chapter are outlined some of the theory and economic interpretation of dual pricing in the linear programming case. The analogues of some of these propositions in the integer programming case are proved and discussed. Our theory is based on four notions:

(1) The resource vector $r$ is far enough into the interior of the cone generated by the columns of $B$,
(2) The dual prices of the linear programming case must be augmented by a finite set of subsidies,
(3) The subsidies are invariant with respect to a certain class of transformations on the resource vector $r$ or the possible point $y$, and
(4) The subsidies are bounded with respect to changes in scale of $r$ or $y$.

Since the resource vector $r$ must lie far enough in the interior of the cone generated by $B$, it applies to only a limited class of integer problems, i.e., those in which the solutions are related to the solutions of linear problems in a systematic way. For a given $r = r^*$, however, if the theory does not hold, it does hold for some $r = \lambda\cdot r^*$ where $\lambda > 1$ represents an increase in scale. That is, if $r^*$ does not lie in $R$, then for some increase in scale $\lambda\cdot r^*$ does lie in $R$. Furthermore as $\lambda$ increases indefinitely, the difference between the integer problem and the straight linear problem becomes insignificant relative to any measure of cost, revenue, or scale.

# CHAPTER 7

## *CONCLUSION*

Writers in economic theory rarely include indivisible commodities in their analysis. There are two plausible explanations for this. First, the tools of algebra and mathematical analysis usually fail to be of much use in analyzing the effects of indivisible commodities. These tools are most useful dealing with continuous concave functions and convex sets. In analyzing indivisibilities, the types of functions with which one is concerned are usually discrete and neither concave nor convex. Sets are not usually convex. Secondly, many writers may feel that indivisible commodities would make no significant difference in their analysis. Either commodity divisibility is assumed to be a sufficient approximation to the real-world phenomena with which they are concerned or the analysis would be identical or similar if commodities were assumed to be discrete. In this volume, the theorems on substitution between divisible and indivisible commodities, the "near profit maximization" theorems, and the body of analysis in Chapter 2, which does not require a divisibility postulate, indicate that in some situations, e.g., where scale is large or where ample opportunities exist for substitution between divisible and indivisible commodities, the presence of indivisible commodities does not make much difference. In general, one might say that the "effects of indivisibilities" (the loss from operating at Pareto optimal but profit maximizing levels of production) tend to remain finite regardless of scale. For a sufficiently large scale the effects of indivisibilities are "averaged out" and their relevance is not so great. In the words of Chamberlin, "the inefficiencies caused by indivisibilities would always be averaged over all units, and would usually become inconsequential for anything but the smallest outputs. Herein lies the justification in most cases for ignoring them. . . ."[1]

### 7.1 Pricing and Increasing Returns

Sometimes one may justifiably ignore the effects of indivisibilities; often, however, failure to include them leads to fallacious or misleading conclusions. At the risk of being imprecise, we can generalize to some extent and say that indivisibilities are important when economies of scale are significant, recognized, and are or ought to be taken into account in formulating production decisions. In such situations the use of fixed prices to guide production decisions does not necessarily produce optimal or near-optimal results.

[1] E. H. Chamberlin, *The Theory of Monopolistic Competition* (7th edn., Cambridge, Massachusetts: Harvard University Press, 1956), pp. 240–241.

In the case of a single-product firm, for example, indivisibilities, economies of scale, and a given set of prices on all inputs result in falling average costs over other ranges of output. The average cost curve has a series of local minima, some of which may be global minima. If the set of production possibilities is additive, global minima occur periodically at regular intervals of output.[2] If output is priced below the global minimum average cost no output is profitable. If price is above the global minimum average cost, it is profitable to expand output without limit. If price is equal to the global minimum average cost, any multiple of a global minimum cost output is profit-maximizing.[3] Under such circumstances a Pareto optimal level of production can only be achieved through a competitive pricing mechanism if it happens to be a multiple of an output at which a global average cost minimum occurs.

In situations where indivisibilities and increasing returns make competitive pricing non-optimal, three approaches have been suggested. First, a system of given fixed prices combined with lump sum subsidies may be used to guide production decisions. The subsidy is not necessarily invariant with respect to the particular optimal production point. In the integer activity analysis case, however, only some finite number of subsidies is required for specified (infinite) sets of possible optimal production points. Second, discriminatory pricing of a particular sort results in optimal production patterns. The first units of an output are sold at a higher price and the first units of inputs purchased at a lower price than the price for additional units of output or input. Third, if commodities are not priced individually but in groups, then in some cases Pareto optimal production is also profit-maximizing.

Examples of actual pricing practices in which discriminatory pricing of the two-part variety described above abound. For example, passenger rates on planes and trains are not a linear function of distance traveled. The first few miles are most costly than succeeding miles. Telephone long distance rates are not a linear function of distance. Group health insurance

[2] See for example, M. L. Joseph, "A Discontinuous Cost Curve and the Tendency to Increasing Returns," *Economic Journal*, Vol. 43 (Sept. 1933); p. 390. "The points of minimum cost where successive numbers of units of fixed plant are employed occur at regular intervals of output" (p. 393), and "as the total output increases, the departures from this optimum line [the line of minimum average cost] become less and less. It is only where the scale of production is extremely large that these departures become negligible and we reach a position of constant costs." See also Charles Babbage, *On the Economy of Machinery and Manufactures* (3rd edn., London: C. Knight, 1833), p. 212. Babbage shows how average cost is minimized at regular intervals of output. In his analysis there are several indivisible inputs and minimum cost occurs whenever output is a multiple of the least common multiple of the output capacity of all the indivisible inputs. He calls this the "law of multiples."

[3] This phenomenon is called by Ivar Jantzen, "The Law of Harmony." See I. Jantzen, "Laws of Production Cost," *Econometrica*, Vol. 16 (Jan. 1948), pp. 44–48, and *Basic Principles of Business Economics abd National Calculation* (Copenhagen: J. Jorgensen and Co. 1939), pp. 30–58. See also Erich Schneider, *Theorie der Produktion* (Vienna and Berlin: 1934), Appendix, "Des Harmoniegesetz," pp. 83–92.

plans are cheaper than individual coverage. The cost of insuring an additional person under a group plan is less than the cost of insuring the initial person. Certain heavy machinery is not priced at a constant price per unit of capacity. The price per unit of capacity for a large capacity unit is less than the price per unit of capacity for a smaller unit.[4] The Wright system of electrical rates is commonly used. The customer is charged "a heavy initial charge for current" and then, pays "a lower rate for additional current."[5]

There are other types of pricing schemes for which the price per unit is high at first and lower for later units of output. For example, the famous "two part tariff" on electricity achieves this result. Each customer is charged an initial fee for electric service and then a given rate per kilowatt-hour.[6] The effective cost per kilowatt-hour is a decreasing function of the number of kilowatt-hours. Another way of achieving an approximation to this result is to charge customers who can be expected to be heavy users of electricity a rate different from the rate charged to users who will most likely use little electricity. Thus industrial customers are often automatically charged less per kilowatt-hour than residential users.[7] Owners of "all-electric homes" receive lower rates than other residential users.[8]

Pricing by groups of commodities is also quite often done and accepted in practice. For example, brokers' fees on security sales differ by the "odd lot" and "round lot." Carloads of oranges are cheaper than less-than-carload lots. Charter airline flights are cheaper per person than individual flights. One can cite examples almost endlessly. The existence of such pricing schemes may be justified by increasing returns.[9]

## 7.2 Scope of the Analysis

This volume does not pretend to be a definitive analysis of the problems associated with indivisibilities. For one thing, consumers have

[4] G. Stigler, *The Theory of Price* (New York: Macmillan and Company, 1952), p. 138. See J. M. Clark, *Studies in the Economics of Overhead Costs* (Chicago: University of Chicago Press, 1933), pp. 416–433, for additional examples of this kind.

[5] J. M. Clark, *op.cit.*, p. 325.

[6] See A. M. Henderson, "The Pricing of Public Utility Undertakings," *The Manchester School of Economics and Social Studies*, Vol. 15 (Sept. 1947), p. 242, pp. 237–239 and W. A Lewis, *op.cit.*, Ch. II.

[7] J. M. Clark, *op.cit.*, p. 426 and A. M. Henderson, *op.cit.*, p. 240.

[8] Consolidated Edison's *Annual Report* (1962), p. 18.

[9] For discussions of the desirability of pricing other than on a traditional marginal cost basis see in particular the discussions between Frisch and Hotelling and Taussig and Pigou, see H. Hotelling, "The General Welfare in Relation to Problems of Taxation and of Railway and Utility Rates," *Econometrica*, Vol. 6 (July 1938), pp. 242–269, R. Frisch, "The Dupuit Taxation Problem," *Econometrica*, Vol. 7 (Ap. 1939), pp. 145–150 and the series of replies and rejoinders in Vol. 7 of *Econometrica*, pp. 151–160. See also F. W. Taussig, "Railway Rates and Joint Cost Once More," *The Quarterly Journal of Economics*, Vol. 27 (Feb. 1913), p. 378, and A. C. Pigou, "Railway Rates and Joint Cost," with a rejoinder by Taussig, *The Quarterly Journal of Economics*, Vol. 27 (Aug. 1913), pp. 687–694.

been virtually ignored. Any general theory will certainly have to deal with both production and exchange. Furthermore, the discussion of integer activity analysis in Chapter 6 is not completely satisfactory since it fails to handle those cases where the optimal values of the non-basic linear programming variables force the basic variables to become negative. Thus when the resource vector $r$ is close to the origin or to the boundary of the cone formed by the basic vectors, the periodicity of the optimal solution is destroyed. To handle such cases, some generalization of the analysis in Chapter 6 may be possible.

Finally, the analysis in all of these chapters has not taken into account the manner in which any system of prices is enforced. The usual assumption in an analysis of a competitive economy is that there is a very large number of small producers, no one of which is able to affect prices by its own production decisions. Where indivisible commodities are present, the only efficient outputs may be multiples of a certain minimum amount. If the particular socially desirable level of output does not happen to be a large enough multiple of this minimum level, then only a small number of firms or individual production units may be possible. In such a case each firm will be "so large that its operations exert a significant influence on price," and "we pass out of the realm of atomistic competition and approach that of partial monopoly."[10]

There is a more subtle variant of this problem. Suppose marginal firms act as if prices were constant, but when they enter the market, prices in fact do change. Prices may change enough so that a marginal firm whose owners had expected to make a profit actually operates at a loss once entry has occurred. Also, it is possible that the price change will be enough to cause some or all of the other firms in the industry to begin operating at a loss, as well, where formerly they were reaping a profit. In the words of Cady:[11]

> "If [a marginal firm] remains aloof, the price is high enough to draw him in; if he comes into the industry, the price falls below his, as well in this case, his competitor's minimum opportunity average cost. This tends to drive him back out. In a situation, however, where markets are large and where there are a few internal economies of scale, the individual producer is small relative to the entire industry, which renders pointless the entire discussion about the problem of the producer who alternately is drawn in and out. No one producer is important enough to spoil the prices for the rest."

Cady adds the warning, however, that the problem may still exist if producers are drawn into the industry and out of the industry in groups.

[10] Jacob Viner, "Cost Curves and Supply Curves," in G. Stigler and K. Boulding, eds., *Readings in Price Theory* (Irwin: Homewood, Illinois, 1952), p. 215.

[11] George Johnson Cady, *Entrepreneurial Cost and Price* (Evanston, Illinois, 1942), p. 41.

The problems of enforcing a system of competitive prices are difficult enough when indivisibilities are present. The systems of discriminatory pricing and of subsidies proposed in this volume pose even more formidable problems. Discriminatory prices can be enforced if it is possible to isolate separate markets and if there is no resale by purchasers in different markets. This type of pricing may be enforced by a monopolist, but there is no assurance that a discriminating monopolist will charge prices which would lead to Pareto optimal production. Rather, a monopolist presumably would charge prices so as to maximize profits. Other than discriminating monopoly, different prices may be enforced by government fiat as is the case with certain types of multiple exchange rate systems which are enforced in the purchase and sale of foreign exchange.

A system of subsidies might also be enforced by government. There are many problems associated with such a system; the effects of subsidies on income distribution and possible interactions between the subsidies and prices are some examples.

The analysis of indivisibilities and their effects on the theory of general equilibrium is extremely difficult. Many questions have been left unanswered. It is the author's hope that this volume has made some contribution in the right direction and will suggest further research in this area.

# *APPENDIX*

## A.1 Vectors and Spaces

Let $y_1, y_2, \ldots, y_n$ be real numbers. Each one of these numbers can represent a co-ordinate in an $n$-dimensional space which we denote by $E^n$. For example, if $n = 2$, then $y_1$ represents the value along the horizontal axis and $y_2$ represents the value along the vertical axis as in Figure A.1. If we choose any point in $E^2$, we represent that point by $(y_1, y_2)$. For example, the point (3, 2) is shown in Figure A.1. Here $y_1 = 3$ and $y_2 = 2$.

In three dimensions, the space is denoted by $E^3$. Such a space may be visualized by imagining a third axis perpendicular to the page and drawn through the origin 0 in Figure A.1. A point in this space is represented by $(y_1, y_2, y_3)$. In $n$-dimensions we can no longer visualize the space $E^n$. A point in this space is represented by $(y_1, y_2, \ldots, y_n)$.

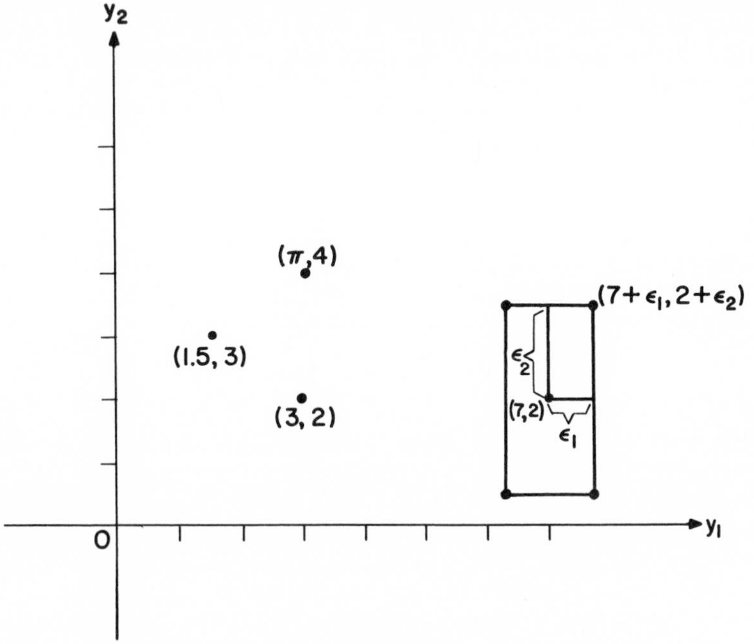


Figure A.1

A point $y = (y_1, y_2, \ldots, y_n)$ is also called a vector in $E^n$.

A.1.1. Multiplication of a vector by a single real number $\lambda$, called a scalar, results in the vector

$$\lambda \cdot y = (\lambda y_1, \lambda y_2, \ldots, \lambda y_n).$$

For example, we may multiply the vector $(5, 4, 3\frac{1}{2})$ by $\frac{1}{2}$ to get the product of a scalar and a vector

$$\tfrac{1}{2}(5, 4, 3\tfrac{1}{2}) = (2\tfrac{1}{2}, 2, 1\tfrac{3}{4}).$$

A.1.2. Multiplication of two vectors $x$ and $y$ results in a product $x \cdot y$ which is a single real number.

$$x \cdot y = x_1 \cdot y_1 + x_2 \cdot y_2 + \cdots + x_n \cdot x_n.$$

For example, the product of $(5, 4, 3\frac{1}{2})$ and $(6, 3\frac{1}{4}, 2)$ is

$$(6, 3\tfrac{1}{4}, 2) \cdot (5, 4, 3\tfrac{1}{2}) = 6 \cdot 5 + 3\tfrac{1}{4} \cdot 4 + 2 \cdot 3\tfrac{1}{2} = 50.$$

A.1.3. The sum of two vectors $x + y$ is another vector

$$x + y = (x_1 + y_1, x_2 + y_2, \ldots, x_n + y_n).$$

Thus

$$(6, 3\tfrac{1}{4}, 2) + (5, 4, 3\tfrac{1}{2}) = (11, 7\tfrac{1}{4}, 5\tfrac{1}{2}).$$

A.1.4. The norm of a vector $y$ is the positive square root of the product of a vector by itself

$$(y \cdot y)^{1/2} = (y_1^2 + y_2^2 + \cdots + y_n^2)^{1/2}.$$

A.1.5. The distance $d$ between two vectors $x$ and $y$ is the norm of the difference $x - y$.

$$\begin{aligned} d &= +[(x - y)(x - y)]^{1/2} \\ &= +[(x_1 - y_1)^2 + (x_2 - y_2)^2 + \cdots + (x_n - y_n)^2]^{1/2}. \end{aligned}$$

For example, the distance between $(6, 3\frac{1}{4}, 2)$ and $(5, 4, 3\frac{1}{2})$ is determined by first calculating the difference

$$(6 - 5, 3\tfrac{1}{4} - 4, 2 - 3\tfrac{1}{2}) = (1, -\tfrac{3}{4}, -1\tfrac{1}{2}).$$

The norm of the difference is the distance

$$(1 + \tfrac{9}{16} + \tfrac{9}{4})^{1/2} = (\tfrac{61}{16})^{1/2}$$

## A.2 Sets and Functions

A set of points in $E^n$ is a collection of points of the form $(y_1, \ldots, y_n)$. The number of points may be finite or infinite. For example, in Figure A.1, the points (3, 2), (1.5, 3), and $(\pi, 4)$ form a finite set of points. The positive portion of the $y_1$ axis is an infinite set of points. All points in the region labelled $A$ in Figure A.2 form an infinite set of points.

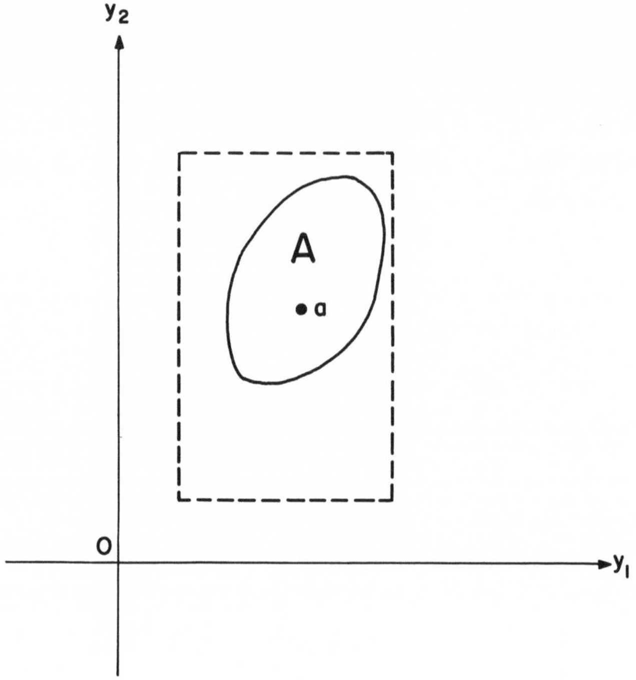


Figure A.2

If a point $y = (y_1, y_2, \ldots, y_n)$ belongs to the set $A$, we write $y \in A$.

A.2.1. If $A$ and $B$ are two sets and if for any $x \in A$ it is always true that $x \in B$, then $A$ is contained in $B$.

In Figure A.3 $A$ is contained in $B$.

A.2.2. If $A$ is contained in $B$ and $B$ is contained in $A$, then $A$ and $B$ are the same set.

A.2.3. The intersection of two sets $A$ and $B$ is the set of points $y$ which belong to both $A$ and $B$.

In Figure A.3, the intersection of sets $C$ and $D$ is the shaded area.

A sequence of points $y^1, y^2, \ldots, y^n$ is said to approach the point $y$ if we can define an arbitrarily small neighborhood around $y$ such that the neighborhood always contains a point of the sequence. Let us consider the point, $(\pi, 4)$ in Figure A.1. The sequence of points $(\pi + 2, 5)$, $(\pi + \frac{2}{3}, 4\frac{1}{2})$, $(\pi + \frac{2}{9}, 4\frac{1}{4})$, $(\pi + \frac{2}{27}, 4\frac{1}{8})$, etc., approaches the point $(\pi, 4)$ since we can always find a point of the sequence in an area around $(\pi, 4)$ regardless of how small the area.

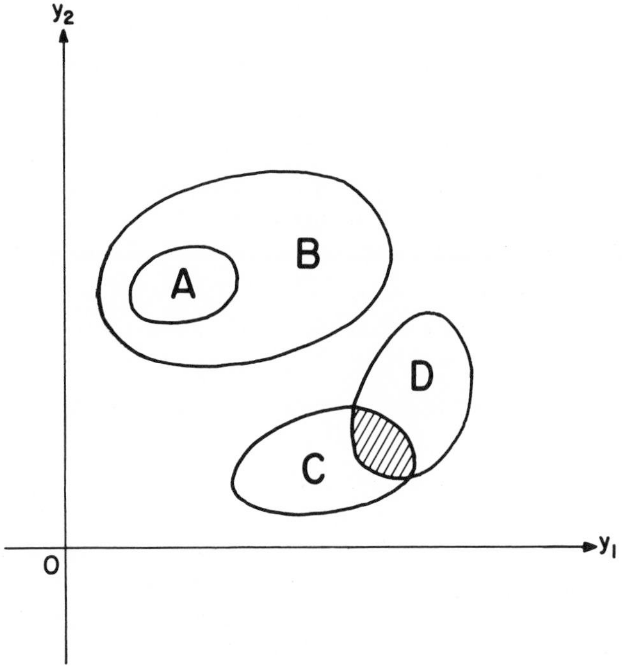


Figure A.3

A.2.4. The set $A$ is closed if $y \in A$ whenever

(*a*) there exists a sequence of points $y^1, y^2, \ldots, y^n$ which approaches the point $y$ such that

(*b*) all of the points in the sequence belong to $A$.

Thus if the set $A$ in Figure A.2 is regarded as the points inside the boundary of $A$ but not the points on the boundary, then this set is not closed. We may find a sequence of points along the line connecting $a$ and any boundary point $b$. Such a sequence approaches the point $b$. Each member of the sequence belongs to $A$, but the boundary point $b$ does not belong to $A$ and the set is not closed.

A.2.5. The closure of the set $A$ written $(A)$ is the smallest closed set which contains $A$.

In Figure A.2, if the set $A$ does not include the boundary but only the points inside the boundary, then the closure of $A$ is the set which contains the boundary and the points inside the boundary.

A.2.6. An $\varepsilon$-neighborhood of any point $x$ is the set of points $y$ where

$$x - \varepsilon \leqq y \leqq x + \varepsilon$$

In Figure A.1, the $\varepsilon$-neighborhood of the point (7, 2) is shown as a rectangle about the point. $\varepsilon$ is a vector $(\varepsilon_1, \varepsilon_2)$ and the $\varepsilon$-neighborhood is the set of points $y = (y_1, y_2)$ satisfying the inequalities.

$$7 - \varepsilon_1 \leqq y_1 \leqq 7 + \varepsilon_1$$
$$2 - \varepsilon_2 \leqq y_2 \leqq 2 + \varepsilon_2$$

A.2.7. The interior of the set $A$, written )A(, is the set of all points of $A$ for which there exists an $\varepsilon$-neighborhood such that every point in the $\varepsilon$-neighborhood is a point of $A$.

A.2.8. The exterior of the set $A$ is the set of all points *not* belonging to $A$ for which there exists an $\varepsilon$-neighborhood such that every point in the $\varepsilon$-neighborhood is *not* a point of $A$.

A.2.9. The boundary of the set $A$ is the set of all points which belong neither to the interior nor the exterior.

In Figure A.2, the interior of $A$ is the set of points inside the curve marking off the boundary. For any point in the interior we can always find a $\varepsilon$-neighborhood, i.e., a rectangle, which includes the point and still lies entirely in the set $A$. Note that for a boundary point, we cannot find such a rectangle. For a boundary point, any rectangle will include points in $A$ as well as points outside $A$. It is easy to prove

THEOREM A.2.1. *A closed set contains its boundary.*

A.2.10. A set $A$ is bounded if there exists an $\varepsilon$-neighborhood about a point $a \in A$ such that the $\varepsilon$-neighborhood contains all the points of A.

In Figure A.2, the set $A$ is bounded since there is a rectangle about $a$ which contains the set $A$ within its boundaries.

A.2.11. A set is compact if it is closed and bounded.

Let $f(y)$ denote a real-valued function defined for vectors $y$ in the space $E^n$. In other words, for each vector $y$ we associate one and only one real number.

A.2.12. The function $f(y)$ is continuous if whenever a sequence $y^1$, $y^2, \ldots, y^q$ approaches $y$, the sequence of numbers $f(y^1) f(y^2), \ldots,$ $f(y^q)$approaches $f(y)$.

The following theorem is stated without proof.

THEOREM A.2.2. *If $f(y)$ is continuous, and if $y \in A$ where $A$ is compact, then $f(y)$ has a minimum and maximum value over all $y \in A$.*

A.2.13. A set $A$ is convex if whenever $x \in A$ and $y \in A$, then $\lambda x + (1 - \lambda)y \in A$ where the scalar $\lambda$ satisfies the inequality $0 \leqq \lambda \leqq 1$.

Thus in Figure A.4, the set $A$ is the enclosed region of $E^2$ labelled $A$. If we connect two points $a$ and $b$ belonging to $A$ by a straight line segment, any point $c$ on this segment is represented by $c = \lambda \cdot a + (1 - \lambda) \cdot b$ where $0 \leqq \lambda \leqq 1$. All such points on the line segment between $a$ and $b$ must belong to the set $A$ itself. Figure A.4 also depicts a set $B$ which is not convex. The line segment connecting two points $a$ and $b$, both of which belong to the set $B$ does not lie entirely in the set $B$.

THEOREM A.2.3. *The intersection of two closed convex sets is closed and convex. If one of the sets is compact, the intersection is compact.*

A.2.14. The convex hull of a set $A$ is the smallest convex set which contains the set $A$.

In Figure A.5, the convex hull of the set $A$ is the set which includes $A$ and the shaded area around $A$. This set is convex and is the smallest possible convex set which contains $A$.

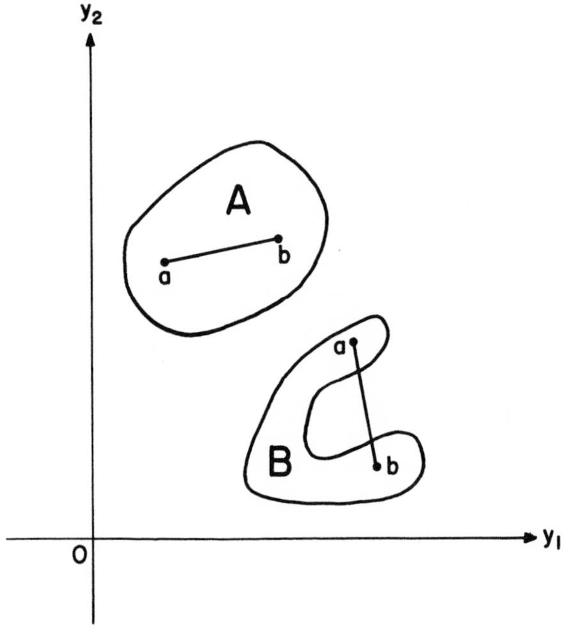


Figure A.4

## A.3 Cones

A.3.1. A set $A$ is a cone if whenever $y \in A$, then $\lambda \cdot y \in A$ where the scalar $\lambda \geqq 0$.

Some examples of cones are shown in Figures A.6 and A.7. The line emanating from the origin and passing through the point $a$ in Figure A.6

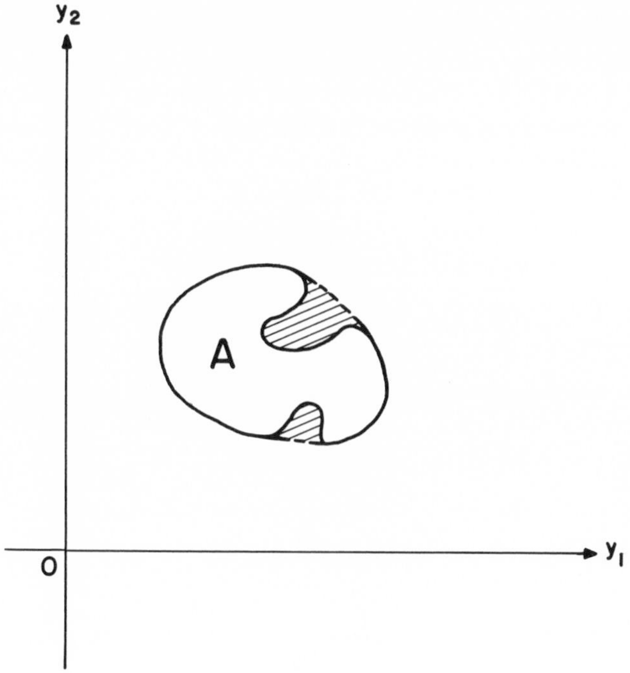


Figure A.5

is a cone. The shaded area in Figure A.6 is a cone. The two shaded areas in Figure A.7 also form a cone and each shaded area individually forms a cone.

A.3.2. The translation of a cone $A$ to the point $a$ is the set of points $x = a + y$ where $a$ is any vector, and $y$ is a point of $A$.

In Figure A.8, the cone $C$ is translated to the point $a$.

A.3.3. The negative of the cone $A$ is written $-A$ and is the set of points $-y$ where $y \in A$.

In Figure A.9, the cone $C$ is "flipped" about the origin to obtain $-C$.

THEOREM A.3.1. *A cone $A$ is convex if and only if the following is satisfied: if $x \in A$ and $y \in A$, then $x + y \in A$.*

*Proof:* Suppose $x + y \in A$ whenever $x \in A$ and $y \in A$. Now if $a \in A$ and $b \in A$, then $\lambda a \in A$ and $(1 - \lambda)b \in A$ by definition. Since $\lambda a + (1 - \lambda)b \in A$ for $0 \leqq \lambda \leqq 1$, the cone $A$ is convex.

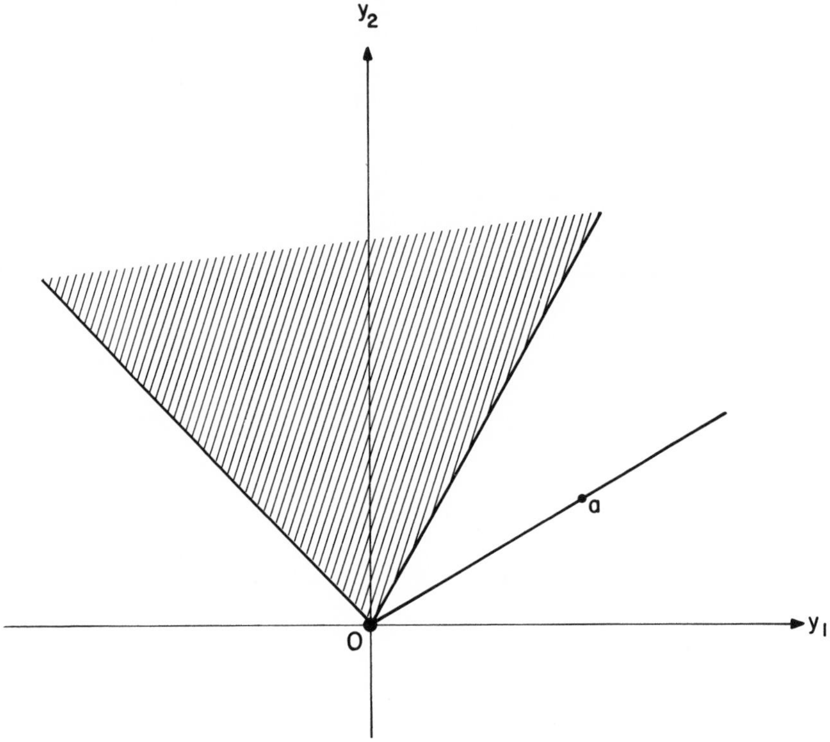


Figure A.6

Now suppose $A$ is convex. Then $\lambda x + (1 - \lambda)y \in A$ when $x \in A$ and $y \in A$. Now $\lambda_1 \cdot x \in A$ and $\lambda_2 \cdot y \in A$ by definition. Furthermore, $\lambda(\lambda_1 x) + (1 - \lambda)(\lambda_2 y) \in A$. Let $\lambda_1 = 1/\lambda$ and $\lambda_2 = 1/(1 - \lambda)$. Then $x + y \in A$ and the theorem is proved.

A.3.4. The ray through a point $y$ is the set of points $x = \lambda \cdot y$ where $\lambda \geqq 0$.

Obviously every cone contains the whole ray through any point of the cone. Furthermore the ray through any point is itself a cone.

A.3.5. The sum $A + B$ of two cones is the set of points $x + y$ where $x \in A$ and $y \in B$.

A.3.6. A polyhedral cone is the sum of a finite number of rays.

In Figure A.10, the cone $C$ is polyhedral since it is the sum of two rays, one through the point $a$ and one through the point $b$. It is therefore easy to prove

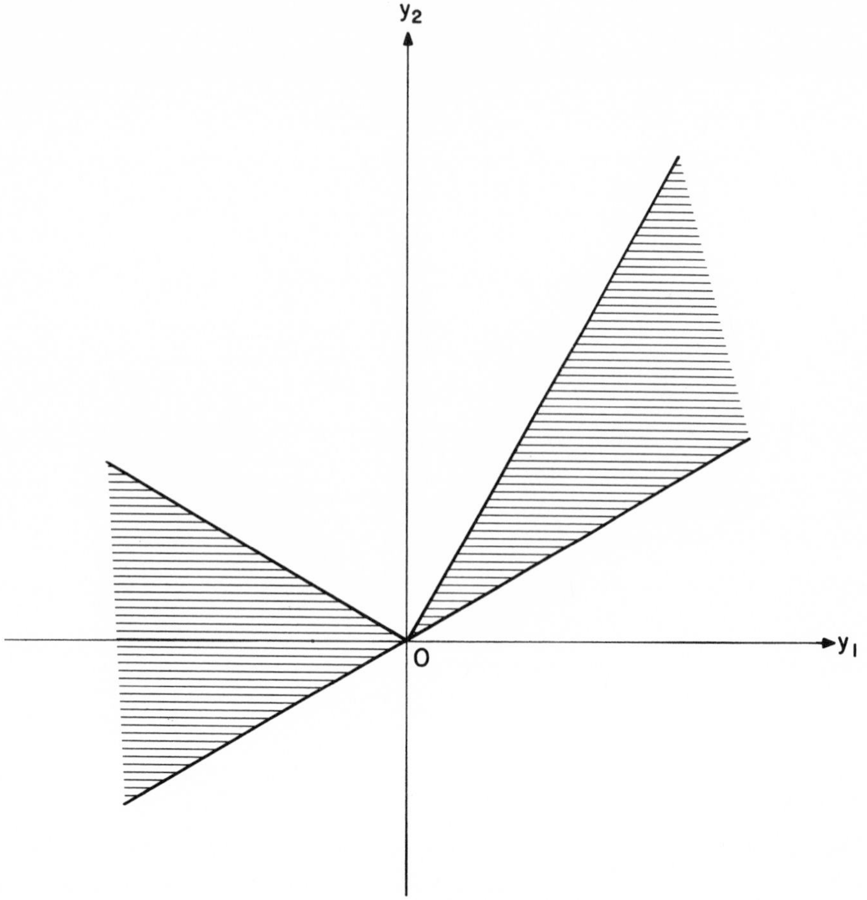


Figure A.7

Theorem A.3.2. *A polyhedral cone is closed and convex.*

A.3.7. The polar of a cone $A$ is written $A^*$ and is the set of points $x$ such that $x \cdot y \leqq 0$ for all $y \in A$.

In Figure A.11, the cone $C$ has as its polar the set of $a$ points such that a ray drawn through such a point forms an obtuse or right angle greater than or equal to 90 degrees.

A.3.8. The set $I$ is the set of all non-negative vectors $y \geqq 0$.

A.3.9. The set $-I$ is the set of all non-positive vectors $y \leqq 0$.

A.3.10. The set $\pm I$ is the whole space $E^n$.

Obviously $+I$, $-I$, and $\pm I$ are convex polyhedral cones. We now prove several important theorems. Some proofs are supplied. For others the proofs

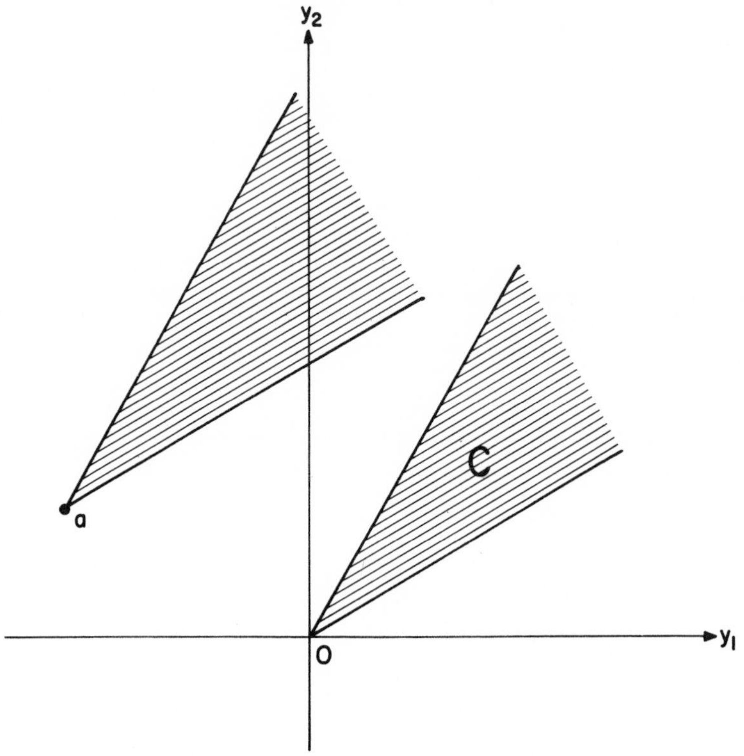


Figure A.8

can be found in Fenchel, Gale or Gerstenhaber[1] or are left to the reader.

THEOREM A.3.3. *If the closed convex cone A is non-empty and there is at least one point a which is exterior to A, then $A^*$ contains at least one point $x \neq 0$.*

*Proof:* Let $R$ be the set of points $y$ where $(a - y).\ (a - y) \leqq r^2$ where $r$ is a real number. This is a sphere of radius $r$ in the space $E^n$ with $a$ as its center. It is easy to show that $B$ is compact and convex. If $r$ is made large enough, the intersection of the cone $A$ and $B$ is compact, convex, and not empty. Let $f(y) = (a - y)\cdot(a - y)$. This function is continuous and therefore has a minimum $f(b) = (a - b)\cdot(a - b)$ over the intersection of $A$ and $B$. In fact the positive square root of $f(y)$ is the distance between $a$ and any point $y$ in the intersection and $b$ minimizes this distance (see Figure A.12). Since $a$ is exterior to the cone, $f(y)$ is continuous, and $f(a) = 0$, the minimum value $f(b) > 0$. Furthermore it is obvious that $f(b)$ is the minimum value of $f(y)$ for all $y \in A$ since by

[1] W. Fenchel, *Convex Cones, Sets, and Functions*, mimeographed, Princeton University Department of Mathematics (Sept. 1963); D. Gale, "Convex Polyhedral Cones and Linear Inequalities," and M. Gerstenhaber, "Theory of Convex Polyhedral Cones," in T. C. Koopmans, ed., *Activity Analysis of Production and Allocation* (New York: Wiley, 1951), pp. 287–316.

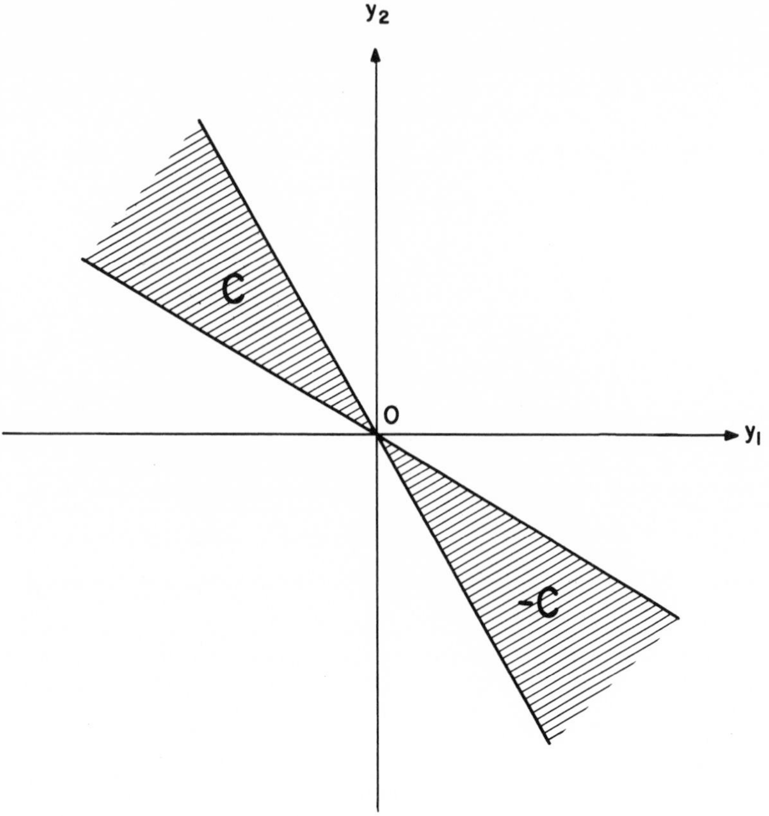


Figure A.9

definition any point outside the sphere $R$ has a value of $f(y) > r^2$ and $f(b) < r^2$.

Now we prove that $(y - b)\cdot(a - b) \leqq 0$ for all $y \in A$. Suppose this were not true. Then $(y^* - b)\cdot(a - b) > 0$ for some $y^* \in A$. Take a convex combination $y^0 = \lambda\cdot y^* + (1 - \lambda)\cdot b \in A$. Then

$$\begin{aligned} f(y^0) &= (a - y^0)\cdot(a - y^0) \\ &= (a - b - \lambda(y^* - b))\cdot(a - b - \lambda(y^* - b)) \\ &= (a - b)\cdot(a - b) - 2\lambda(y^* - b)\cdot(a - b) \\ &\quad + \lambda^2(y^* - b)\cdot(y^* - b). \end{aligned}$$

When $\lambda = 0$, we have $f(y^0) = (a - b)\cdot(a - b) = f(b)$. The first derivative of $f(y^0)$ with respect to $\lambda$ is $f'(y^0) = -2(y^* - b).\ (a - b) + 2\lambda(y^* - b)\cdot(y^* - b)$. When $\lambda = 0$, we have

$$f'(y^0) = -2(y^* - b)(a - b) < 0.$$

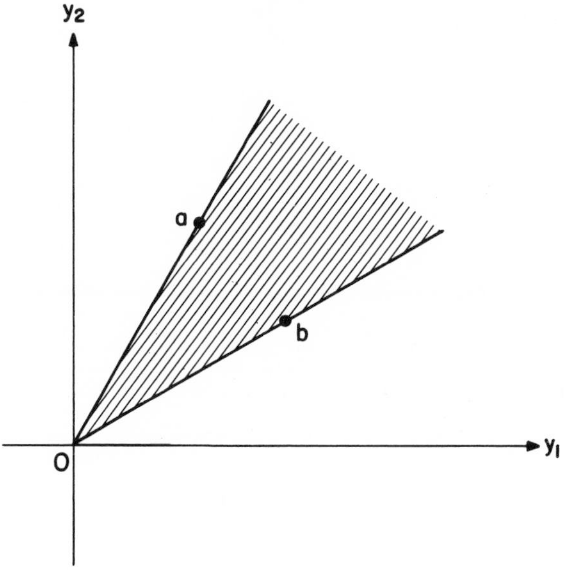


**Figure A.10**

Using a continuity argument we can show that for some $\lambda$ in the interval $0 \leqq \lambda \leqq 1$, $f(y^0) < f(b)$. This contradicts, however, our assumption that $f(b)$ is the minimum value of $f(y)$ for all $y \in A$. Thus $(y - b)\cdot(a - b) \leqq 0$ for all $y \in A$.

Now $y = 0 \in A$. Then $(0 - b)\cdot(a - b) \leqq 0$ or $b\cdot(a - b) \geqq 0$. Then let $y = b + b$ which belongs to $A$ since $A$ is a convex cone. $(2b - b)\cdot(a - b) \leqq 0$ or $b\cdot(a - b) \leqq 0$. Thus $b\cdot(a - b) = 0$.

On the other hand, $(y - b)\cdot(a - b) \leqq 0$ for all $y \in A$ or $y(a - b) - b(a - b) \leqq 0$ or $y\cdot(a - b) \leqq 0$. Thus $x = (a - b)$ belongs to $A^*$ and since $a \neq b$, we have $x = (a - b) \neq 0$. The theorem is proved. The next theorem follows immediately.

THEOREM A.3.4. *If $A$ is a closed convex cone $A^{**} = A$. If $A$ is not closed,* $A^{**} = (A)$.

*Proof:* Let $a$ be any point not in $A$. Since $A$ is closed the point $a$ is exterior to $A$. Using the same construction as in Theorem A.3.3, the vector $(a - b) \in A^*$ and since $y\cdot(a - b) \leqq 0$ for all $y \in A$, the points $y \in A$ must be points of $(A^*)^*$. Thus $A$ is contained in $(A^*)^*$. On the other hand since $b\cdot(a - b) = 0$ and

$$\begin{aligned}(a - b)\cdot(a - b) &= a\cdot(a - b) - b\cdot(a - b)\\ &= a\cdot(a - b) = f(b) > 0\end{aligned}$$

the point $a$ could not possibly belong to $(A^*)^*$. Thus any point not in $A$ is not a point of $(A^*)^*$ and $(A^*)^*$ is contained in $A$. This proves the theorem.

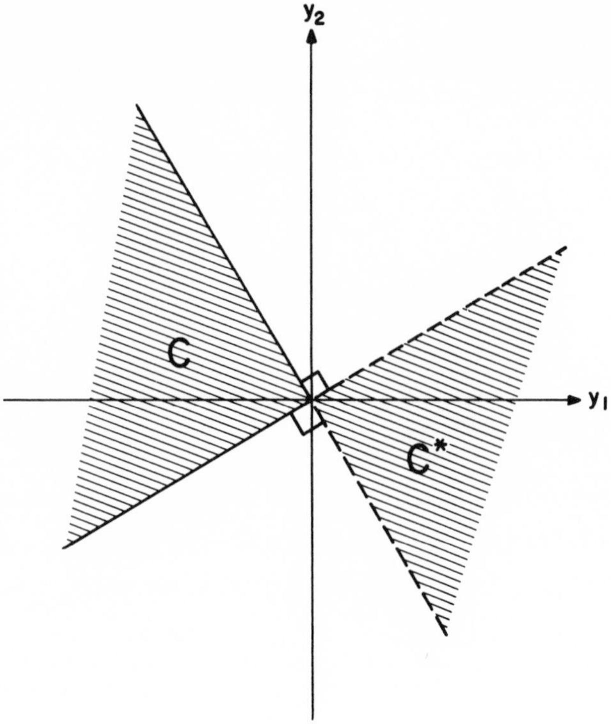


Figure A.11

THEOREM A.3.5. *If $A$ and $B$ are cones,* $(A + B)^* = A^* \cap B^*$.
*Proof:* If $x \in (A + B)^*$, then $x \cdot (a + b) \leqq 0$ for all $a \in A$ and $b \in B$. In particular, if $b = 0$, then $x \cdot a \leqq 0$ for all $a \in A$, and if $a = 0$, then $x \cdot b \leqq 0$ for all $b \in B$. Thus for every $x \in (A + B)^*$, it follows that $x \in A^*$ and $x \in B^*$, or $x \in A^* \cap B^*$. In other words, $(A + B)^*$ is contained in $A^* \cap B^*$. Conversely, if $x \in A^* \cap B^*$, then $x \cdot a \leqq 0$ for every $a \in A$ and $x \cdot b \leqq 0$ for every $b \in B$. That is, $x \cdot (a + b) \leqq 0$. Thus $A^* \cap B^*$ is contained in $(A + B)^*$.

THEOREM A.3.6. *If $A$ and $B$ are convex polyhedral cones then the sum $A + B$ is closed.*

THEOREM A.3.7. *If $A$ is a polyhedral cone, then $A^*$ is a polyhedral cone.*

THEOREM A.3.8. *If $A$ and $B$ are polyhedral cones, the sum $A + B$ is a convex polyhedral cone.*

THEOREM A.3.9. *If $A$ and $B$ are convex polyhedral cones, then* $(A \cap B)^* = A^* + B^*$. *If $A$ and $B$ are closed convex cones, then* $(A \cap B)^* = (A^* + B^*)$.
*Proof:* This theorem follows directly from Theorems A.3.4 and A.3.5 for $(A \cap B)^* = (A^{**} \cap B^{**})^* = (A^* + B^*)^{**} = (A^* + B^*)$.

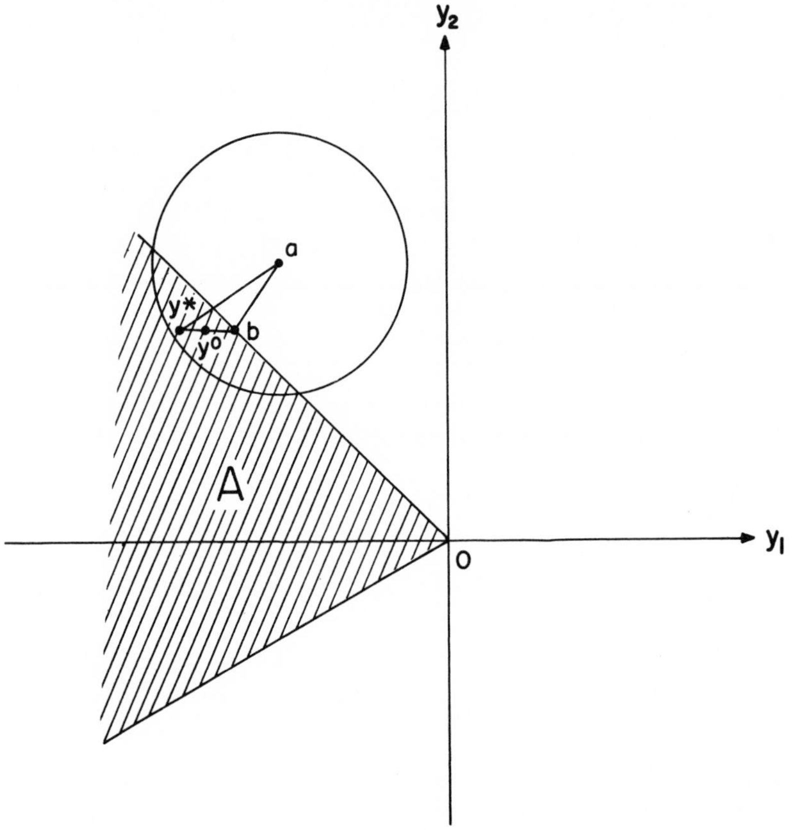


Figure A.12

THEOREM A.3.10. *If $A - B = \pm I$, and if $B$ has an interior, then there exists a vector $x \neq 0$ such that $x \in A \cap )B($.*

*Proof:* Suppose $a_1 \in A$ and $b_1 \in )B($. Now $-a_1 + b_1 \in \pm I$. Since $A - B = \pm I$, there exists an $a_2 \in A$ and a $b_2 \in B$ such that $a_2 - b_2 = -a_1 + b_1$, or $a_1 + a_2 = b_1 + b_2$. Since $b_1$ lies in the interior of $B$, the vector $b_1 + b_2$ lies in the interior of $B$. Thus $x = a_1 + a_2 = b_1 + b_2 \in A \cap )B($.

THEOREM A.3.11. *If $A$ is a convex cone then $A$ contains the interior of the closure of $A$.*

Now we are able to prove the first part of the fundamental theorem discussed in Chapter 5.

THEOREM A.3.12. *Let $C$ be a closed convex cone. Suppose $y^* \in C$ and there exists no $y \in C$ such that $y \geq y^*$. Let $A$ be the set of vectors $t \cdot (y - y^*)$ where $t > 0$ is a scalar and $y \in C$. This cone $A$ is called the local possible cone. Then* *there exists a vector* $p > 0$ *such that* $p \cdot y^* = 0 \geqq p \cdot y$ *for all* $y \in C$ *if and only if* $(A) \cap I = 0$.

*Proof:* Suppose $(A) \cap I = 0$. Then $((A) \cap I)^* = 0^* = \pm I$. Obviously $(A)$ is a closed convex cone and from Theorem A.3.9, $((A) \cap I)^* = ((A)^* + I^*) = \pm I$. Since the interior of $\pm I$ is the set $\pm I$ itself, the interior of $((A)^* + I^*)$ is $\pm I$. By Theorem A.3.11, $(A)^* + I^* = (A)^* - I$ contains $\pm I$. Thus $(A)^* - I = \pm I$. From Theorem A.3.10, it follows that $(A)^*$ contains an interior point of $I$, i.e., a vector $p > 0$. Since $A$ is contained in $(A)$, it follows that $p \cdot t(y - y^*) \leqq 0$ for all $y \in C$ and $t > 0$. Since $0 \in C$, for $t = 1$ we have $p \cdot y^* = 0$ and $p \cdot y \leqq p \cdot y^* = 0$.

On the other hand suppose $(A) \cap I \neq 0$. Thus $a \geq 0$ for some $a \in (A)$. Now $a - \varepsilon$ for some $\varepsilon \neq 0$ lies in $A$. Therefore $a - \varepsilon = t^0(y^0 - y^*)$ for some $t^0 > 0$ and some $y^0 \in C$. Choose $\varepsilon$ small enough so that $p \cdot (a - \varepsilon) > 0$. Then since $a - \varepsilon = t^0(y^0 - y^*)$ for some $t^0 > 0$ and some $y^0 \in C$, we have

$$p \cdot t^0(y^0 - y^*) > 0$$

or

$$p \cdot (y^0 - y^*) > 0 \quad \text{for } y^0 \in C.$$

This shows that for no $p > 0$ is it true that $p \cdot y^* \geqq p \cdot y$ for all $y \in C$.

The sufficiency of conditions (*b*) and (*c*) in the fundamental theorem of Chapter 5 (pp. 64–65) are shown in the following two theorems.

Theorem A.3.13. *If all the assumptions of Theorem A.3.12 hold and if C is polyhedral, then* $(A) \cap I = 0$.

*Proof:* First, $A \cap I = 0$ since if $a \geq 0$ for some $a \in A$, then $t^0(y^0 - y^*) \geq 0$ for some $t^0 > 0$ and $y^0 \in C$. Thus $y^0 \geq y^*$ which contradicts one of the assumptions in Theorem A.3.12. Furthermore $A$ is polyhedral and thus closed so that $(A) \cap I = 0$.

Theorem A.3.14. *Let C be a closed convex cone. Suppose* $y^* \in C$ *and there exists no* $y \in C$ *such that* $y \geq y^*$. *If, for all i, commodity i is an indirect substitute*[2] *for every commodity j for which* $y_j^* \geqq 0$ (*resp.* $\leqq 0$), *then there exists a vector* $p > 0$ *such that* $p \cdot y^* = 0 \geqq p \cdot y$ *for all* $y \in C$.

*Proof:* Consider the set $A - I$ where $A$ is the local possible cone (see Theorem A.3.12). If $p$ is in the polar of $A - I$, then $p \geqq 0$. Otherwise $p \cdot (y + w) > 0$ for some $w$ in $-I$ whose component $w_i$ is arbitrarily large in absolute value. Then $p$ could not be in the polar.

It is easy to show that $p \cdot y^* = 0$. Thus $p_i > 0$ for some $i$ such that $y_i^* \geqq 0$ (resp. $\leqq 0$). Otherwise $p \cdot y^* < 0$ (resp. $> 0$) which is not possible.

[2] See Chapter 4 for a definition of the substitution relationship between two commodities.

Furthermore $p > 0$. Suppose this were not true and $p_j = 0$ while $p_k > 0$ where $y_k^* \geqq 0$ (resp. $\leqq 0$). Then substitution implies that there exists a point $y^{**}$ such that $y_k^{**} > y_k^*$ and $y_i^{**} \geqq y_i^*$ for all $i \neq j$. Then $p \cdot y^{**} > p \cdot y^*$ or $p \cdot (y^{**} - y^*) > 0$ which is not possible if $p$ is in the polar of $A - I$.

Thus if $p$ is in the polar of $A - I$, $p > 0$ and $p \cdot y^* = 0 \geqq p \cdot y$ for all $y$ in $C$. From Theorem A.3.3, a point in the polar exists and the present theorem is proved.

# *INDEX*